Inflorescence

By

Creative Writing Students of La Quinta High School

La Quinta High School
Westminster, California

Inflorescence

Edited and compiled by: Amanda LaPera
Senior Copy Editors: Hillary Nguyen, Jacqueline Truong
Copy Editors: Brandon Nguyen, Thomas Tran
Section Editors: Sydney Dao, Keanu Hua, Michelle Lam, Teresa Le, Bethanie Luu, Hillary Nguyen, Kayla Nguyen, Kellan Nguyen, Jacqueline Truong
Cover Designed by: Kellan Nguyen
Interior Editor: Khanh Tran

Published by La Quinta High School Creative Writing Class

Dedicated to the buds yet to blossom

TABLE OF CONTENTS

GARDEN WITH BUTTERFLIES

by Jacqueline Truong

(Based on Vincent van Gogh's "Garden with butterflies" 1889)

At the beginning of
winter, the garden
was left flowerless
and lonely.

I yearned for warmth.
Few fare well
in the cold.
Yet I searched
in the sea of dead grass.

And in that field
laid two small bodies——
pale, weak, and shallow
of breath.

PHOTOSYNTHESIS

by Kayla Nguyen

I am a tree
with hundreds of branches,
thousands of leaves.

When the crispy golden ball
rises from its slumber,
I absorb its light with
my verdant leaves.

Alas, to steal
from something so bright
a necessary sin.
The ground goes first,
cracking and crumbling.

My leaves fall
like the hair on an old man.
Roots grow thirsty
And my trunk flaky.

I was a tree.
Now, my worth is
just kindling.
I stole from the sun,
so now it burns me.

THE LAST MEAL YOU MADE FOR ME

by Michelle Lam

You told me I couldn't do anything
So, I didn't.
I sat still and ate quietly
Hoping you couldn't hear me.

You told me I couldn't think anything
So, I didn't.
As the man slipped into your room
Then left, splattered on the wall,
A beautiful, ethereal red bloom.

You told me I couldn't say anything
So, I didn't.
When they came and asked questions
I dried my eyes and held my tongue
Because I remembered your lessons.

You told me this, you told me that
So, I've done nothing.
Just like you've said.

Your body is rotting,
Reeking of overripe berries
I sat still and ate quietly

NOT ALWAYS SWEET

by Hillary Nguyen

i've never liked
cookie-cutter phrases
that tell you what to say.

everyone's different, after all.
how can one phrase satisfy so many people
all with different experiences?

but then i got to know you
and all your vulnerabilities,
your past experiences,
so i wished that those
cookie-cutter phrases *did* work,
but of course, they won't work on you.

endless apologies on my end,
even though they're all things i can't control,
even though it's not my fault
for things that happened to you
before we met.

and i don't know what to say.
of course, i say i'll be by your side;
i'll still stay by your side,
forever and always,
but that's it.

i'm left waiting
as you stand there with no response.
i can't tell what you're thinking
and that terrifies me.

there's no sugar-coating it.

life is not always sweet,
not just a bunch of cookies
to eat to make you feel better.
people try to only say the positive things
and give too much sugar

but the thing is,
it has to be said:
there are the bitter things in life,
sour things that make us flinch,
salty things that make us cry,
and things that don't have a taste;

i'll never know what to say,
what's the right thing to say?
so i look at you.
i can help all i can
but no matter what i say,
no matter what others say,
you're the one who has the final say.

you're the only one who can change your life.

GHOST OF FAMILY LOVE
by Ery Nguyen

THE SUN HAD FALLEN under the horizon, dusk imminent as Kine Lyne sipped his fourth cup of tea. He was alone in the kitchen when, for the third time today, a door upstairs slammed shut. At twenty-nine years old, he considered himself too old to believe in ghosts or haunted houses but now wondered if those sorts of superstitions were true. The first time these strange occurrences happened he had brushed them off as the settling of an old house. Now, however, he had suspicions that an unnatural force was in his house.

Which was stupid, and maybe insane. Maybe the lack of social interaction had gotten to him. He hadn't talked to his family in a while, lost in work and stress. He also hadn't talked to his friends, who tried to keep in touch with him even as he ghosted their messages for days on end. Hah. Ghosted. Well, either way, no one else had been in the house since he bought it and moved in.

He'd chosen this house because it was in a quiet neighborhood, with quiet neighbors, and quiet streets. No one would bother him here. Even with mounting evidence that there was a ghost, he couldn't say he regretted buying the house, but he was definitely annoyed.

The lights in the kitchen started to flicker, on and off, on and off, over and over until black spots appeared in his vision and his eyes ached from the rapid flashing. He stumbled out of the kitchen and used the wall to pad his way upstairs, eyes closed to block out any lights that might flicker.

His head spun, dizzy with vertigo. God, he couldn't remember the last time he drank water, nor when he ate. Did he sleep at all last night? When was the last time he showered?

A cold brass doorknob knocked against his hand. He twisted open the door and shuffled inside, and felt the wood of his wardrobe to his left. The light switch at his back clicked on and off. The rumble of his phone's notification sounded from his bed, and, with fumbling hands, he made his way to his bathroom.

At last, he opened his eyes and looked to his mirror, disoriented from his lack of vision.

His own pale face looked back at him, harsh bags under dark brown eyes and the approach of wrinkles across his forehead. Brown hair brushed against his shoulders, hair care forgotten in the midst of work with the addition of a new anxiety and annoyance. He looked like he had died two months ago and forgot to be buried, his body strained with sleep deprivation.

The light in the bathroom flickered, and he groaned into his hands. Something downstairs shattered, like a mirror or a glass cup. Doors slammed shut and furniture crashed to the floor, lights on, off, on, off, on, off, on, off—

"I get it! I get it. You can stop now." He coughed. His voice died out as exhaustion washed over him as a static noise in his ears and an itch across his skin. He pressed his forehead against the cold porcelain of the sink, which comforted his tired mind. Everything continued to crash around him.

"If you're going to torture me with broken furniture, could you at least spare the electricity bill? I got this house because it was cheap, not to overuse the light switches," he mumbled.

He slid down from the sink and lay on the floor, crumpled into a loose ball. Miraculously, the light switches stopped. In fact, as the static noise in his ears died down, he couldn't hear any noise from anywhere in the house. Why … why was it silent?

He pushed himself off the tile, the itch across his skin gone, and wandered out into his bedroom. All the furniture had been pushed over and toppled across the floor, to the point where even the bed had been flipped on its side. His phone, however, was on the floor without a single scratch.

With a sigh, he grabbed the device and pocketed it. As quietly as he could, he shuffled out into the hallway and to the stairs, an upset tightness in his chest at the sight of broken lights and cracked walls. The silence struck fear into his heart, the sudden stillness to the house a stark contrast to the cacophony of sound before. Why had the ghost stopped? Was it planning something?

Once he stepped into the kitchen, he stopped. The temperature in the room was freezing. Where the coffee table was before, was an unbroken mirror. It faced towards the ceiling. He approached it and looked into it, but the reflection staring back at him wasn't his.

Instead, a woman, gaunt, pale, and sickly with long black hair and eyes like the void, peered through the mirror as if it were a window. Was the woman stuck? Or was she in front of him, only appearing in the mirror?

He was startled when the woman spoke.

"Kine Lyne," she rasped.

Her voice had an echo and hushed tone, as if wind had taken her words and whispered them back to her, her mouth barely moved as she stated his name. Her eyes stared at him, glared into his very soul. He kneeled by the mirror and figured if he were to die by a ghost, he wouldn't do so with fear.

The woman's gaze followed him.

"Do you know who I am?" she whispered.

She spoke quietly, yet loud enough for him to hear. And perhaps it was rude of him to not know a resident of the house, former or otherwise, but...

"No, I don't," he uttered and with a dry throat, he continued, "The landlord probably said your name, or something about the house, but I didn't really care back then. I was more interested in buying the house as quickly as possible. I'm, uh, really sorry."

She shook her head. There wasn't a smile on her face, but there wasn't a frown either. More like an apathetic neutral ground, and he was grateful for her lack of care.

"I didn't expect you to know who I am," she admitted, "I lived here with my family a long time ago. One day, we were forced out, and then split apart as we tried to find somewhere safe. My siblings and parents were gone. I searched for them, but I couldn't find them so I came back to this house, hoping that perhaps my family would return home. To the place we loved. I died alone, in this house."

18

Her face scrunched up, an expression that looked like anger and sadness, but even then, her voice was devoid of emotion.

"When I woke up here, dead but alive as a ghost, I moved around the furniture as it was in my old home, slammed the doors open and shut like my siblings would when we played. Mama and Papa always yelled at us when we flipped the light switches."

In an instant, tears flowed down her face and dropped onto the surface of the mirror, and her voice shook the reflection as it rose in volume.

"And then you came along. You, with your worry and your work and your fear of your friends and family," she spat, "I would kill to have what you have now. A way for your loved ones to reach you. To know where your family is. It made me so angry. It made me so, so *angry*."

The destroyed cupboards started to shake again. The light switch flickered in tandem with the shaking mirror and the trembles that overtook the woman.

He had no words nor comfort for the woman, so he sat and watched and ached. It took a moment before she quieted down, the chaos of anger gone. He found his voice, and fumbled through his words.

"I'm sorry," he whispered, "It—it must've been hard to watch me push away everyone I love, especially with what you went through."

He looked down to the mirror, that same exhaustion in his eyes reflected by the woman. Tears started to drip from his face onto the mirror's surface, an ache in his bones and a guilt in his heart.

"It's been a lot these past months. I don't know why. It's just so hard to connect with my family and friends again after moving here. I'm sorry you had to watch me push them away."

He looked at the woman, her head bowed and her hair a curtain around her face.

"Can you tell me your name?"

"Pearl Celes. I'm sorry about what I've done. I got angrier than I should have. You didn't ignore your family for harmful reasons, and my tantrums didn't help, did they?" she whispered.

He brushed away the last of his tears, relieved to know that Pearl was no longer angry. She looked less like a vengeful ghost and more of a sad, lost woman who missed her family. He missed his family too, even if he was so buried in his work and stress that he never realized it.

The phone in his pocket buzzed with a notification, and he froze. It didn't buzz again. A message, either from his family or his friends.

Pearl sniffed and wiped away her own tears. Then, as best as she could, her eyes pinned him with a stern glare so harsh that he wondered if she was ever a mother in her past life.

"If you don't respond, I will destroy everything," she said. "I kept your phone intact for a reason."

He coughed nervously into his hand and took his phone out, the screen illuminating the dim room. It was a goodnight message from his sister, the same message that she always sent around this time. The short text was enough to send fear and anxiety into his heart, and for a moment he considered not replying. It was late, there was no reason why he should keep his sister up at night when they both had work the next day, but Pearl's eyes pierced into his soul.

With quick and shaky hands, he sent back a text, the first response in many weeks, and turned his phone down to the floor. His phone buzzed in only a few seconds, and with it came dread. But there was a comfort, to know that his sister was willing to talk with him after how long he'd been silent, and even Pearl looked happy for him.

"You can stay here if you want, Pearl. It's still your house," he insisted.

Pearl shook her head.

"It's okay, Kine. All I wanted was for you to get back with your family," she said.

With a small, content smile, she disappeared and the room was no longer freezing. He looked down at his phone again, a returned message in his notifications, both upset and happy. He left the kitchen to his bedroom and ignored the destruction all around him. He could worry about cleaning up later. He had a family to reconnect with.

I BITE AT THE HAND THAT FEEDS ME

by Kellan Nguyen

it starts with love,
as everything always does,
and it ends with love,
as most things will,
perhaps, die without.

'it' being how i dig my teeth
through anything i can get my hands on,
the canines tearing through skin
and piercing the heart.
the heart of what, exactly?

just the heart. and the way i can't stop,
can't stop myself from digging through viscera
and looking for something to drown myself in,
something holy and devastating enough
to help me forget everything.

it is love, or perhaps the absence of it,
that makes me so ravenous,
gives me an appetite
doomed to be insatiable,
makes me covet the heart
that can never satisfy me,

gives me the teeth
that can tear through my life
and leave me hungrier than ever.
give me a city and i'll eat it, all of it.
give me a planet and i'll eat it.

let me eat life away slowly

to savor the feeling of it heavy on my tongue,
to extend this wretched life of mine
until a moment comes where i can feel something, anything,
it doesn't matter if it's pain or joy
or anything in between.

the crux of it all is love.
i'll eat everything until i feel it.
the canvas of life peeling off the board,
the paint unsticking and flaking off,
the skin melting.

god, how everything fails
to fill my decrepit chest, the cavity
where my heart used to dwell
before it surrendered and returned to dust.

how everything feeds
the gaping emptiness inside.
there's nothing to do besides eat,
even for all its futility, because if i don't have the lack of love,
i have something much worse.

the pieces of myself i break off like bread
to feed this aching, the pieces of others
i gouge off to feel full—
i wonder where they go sometimes,
wonder what happens when the void consumes them
and doesn't even bother to leave ash behind.

maybe there is a god
sitting in his high heaven, cutting my stories apart
to dine on them to feed his own hunger.
not even the divine can quell this desire, i think.

its claws dig into my chest
like it, too, is eating me alive.
if i fight back enough, i wonder
if i can eat it in turn.

want—to sate it or stoke it.

to have it die, and perhaps me alongside it,
or to have it flare up and burn brighter than flames.
give me peace, and thus, love.
give me fire and brimstone.
maybe i'll eat them both.

would that mean to be full for the first time,
to taste victory? it smells sour and rotten, desire decayed.
it smells like the emptiness winning.
there's no in-between here, no gods or monsters among men.

i don't think i want to play this game anymore.
i don't want this hunger eating my insides away.
let the emptiness eat me
eat the emptiness, eat the desire.
let me be devoid of hunger
and therefore, satisfied and therefore, whole again.
i just don't want to starve anymore.

SELF-CONTRADICTING

by Hillary Nguyen

Such conflicting feelings
A paradox
A self-contradictory being

Wanting to be remembered
But holding the belief that
Friends and family should forget

So reckless
Ready to rush in
But afraid of everything

Those mantras of deep breaths:
Ten seconds in
Five seconds, hold
Ten seconds out,
Couldn't help

Refusing to disappear,
But fading from existence
Feels like the best outcome sometimes

A pulsing pain
That twists and turns in the stomach

A shame that festers in the brain
And squirms despite
The clear love shown
The obvious reassurance that
They will all be there.

But no, it still insists

That they will leave
And if they don't leave,
I will leave first
For how could such a being
Be worthy of these people?

Sleep it off.
A form of escapism

It's terrifying to think about it
So, flight is instinctive
Fleeing from it all

And when the pain pulls back
And the shame hesitates
And that living being is ready,
Even for just a brief moment
Before the cycle starts again,
They will be right there
With open arms

For despite such
Self-contradictions,
Realization dawns:
They will always be there for me.

LET US BE YOUR BOUQUET

by Stella Nguyen

A gladiolus,
So red and bright,
A shoulder to lean on when the bluebells cry
Your petals are fiery, filled with passion and light,
So beautiful, it truly is a sight.
And yet, so chivalrous
To put their needs above yours,
So why is your pain locked behind vitae doors?

You collapse upon the bed; pollen dies as you pour
Your tears, your fears crash against mossy floor
Oh, dear gladiolus, why do you sob?
All alone, your lovely petals torn off

But let us lend you the sun, the soil, the earth.
Let us be your marigold, your light, your strength.

Stubborn you are, but I shall be here
I'll sit beside you as we wait for the future to near.
You sob in silence, and I shall listen
For your fears are mine, and I wish to be your haven.
Your worries are not frivolous
My arms wrap around your shoulders
We'll shake away the pests
That chew on your stem,
You will grow new petals
Love yourself like you love your friends
Share your strength, your troubles
Let me be your lavender

A gladiolus

Passionate, fiery, enchanting
A fighter, a lover, a listener
Yet, alone, it should not be.
Paired with marigolds
Petals hug closely
And perhaps, there is room for lavender
In this sea of sunset and cherry red,
Can I be an elegant pink?
Or the color of cotton?
Flowering in the wisps of evening,
Standing tall besides the gladiolus,
colors intermingle.

This batch of flowers, not so different from the others,
Sit hand in hand.
Let us be your hydrangea
Together, soft fragrance flows openly
Let us be your bouquet
Together in hand.

ONLY A FEW YEARS TO LIVE

by Andy Nguyen

All lives are precious.
Be it ten years or ten seconds,
Cherish life because it could end at any moment.
Don't dwell on negative thoughts, live under a bright light.
Everyone can try their best.
Friends will cheer you on but can't when you're beyond the grave.
Gods made a world for you to live in, not to take yourself out of.
Help is close by, there are people willing to give you their time.
In a few years from now, it will get better.
Just stand up strong, you will realize how capable you really are.
Know that we are all human and we all make mistakes.
Love is near, take time to find someone.
Many things are left for you to experience.
Never give up, the world needs you.
Open up about your problems, we can share burdens.
People aren't perfect, it's okay to fail.
Quote your favorite phrase, use as motivation to make it through the day.
Remember the happy moments, even if they only last a few seconds.
Start your career path, follow your dreams, find what makes you happy.
Try to take breaks, you deserve it.
Ugly is subjective, everyone is beautiful.
Very few people realize how breathtaking you are.
When worse comes to worst, I know you can turn the situation around.
Xanadu is a place of beauty and luxury, find where you are comfortable.
You are amazing in every way, don't believe what other people think.
Zero people who want to bring you down matter.

SOMEPLACE

by Sonny Le

(Based on the painting "Starry Night" by Vincent van Gogh)

A place
Cloaked in darkness
With a dreamy view
Someday, the place I long for
Will show itself to me

To live someplace else
Where stars bring me peace
Replacing the space
That surrounds my mistakes

I found a place to be,
Somewhere to belong
This quiet space
Is all I long for,

Darkness comforts me
As I gaze at the stars
And think to myself
This is a fantasy
In which I now live

THE MEMORY OF YOU

by Yathy Le

On solemn nights like these,
I often find my heart likes to sing its musings
and the lyrics uttered are those of sweet reminiscence.
In one way or another, it would all come back
to the wonder that is you.

Maybe it's the way you stir the butterflies in my stomach
when you smile, or perhaps it's the words you speak,
embroidered with gentle sincerity.
Your star-filled eyes put me in an enamored haze,
which makes me think, there aren't nearly enough
stars in the sky to count all of the things I love about you.

This heart of mine—well, it will sing again and again,
so, I'll bid farewell to these nights of lovesick longing,
and in its place are pleasant thoughts of you.
Gazing up at the vastness above,
I close my eyes with a smile on my face.

SHUTTERED LIGHT

by Bethanie Luu

XIAOWEN AWOKE TO RAGE.

Startled, he bolted upright, hand scrabbling for—*what? A weapon? A sword?*—except nothing was there. By then, the burn of anger against his eyelids had already begun to fade. In its place, bewilderment.

Above him stretched a wide expanse of blue sky and beneath him, sand that contrasted the dark grays of his hanfu. Waves crashed against the shoreline. They appeared almost holographic.

And from behind him, "Oh!"

He squinted his eyes against the sunlight and saw her. Eyes the color of gold and snowy hair, long and untamed.

"You're not human," was the first thing Xiaowen said to her.

"No," she agreed—because even in her semblance to a woman, it was obviously true. Nestled in her locks twitched pointed ears while several fox tails curled and swayed around her feet. And each time she moved, the little bells entwined in her fur and hair rang: *ting-ting.*

She crouched down. Examined him. Smiled, before standing and offering him a hand. "Well, come on now. We should get going before dark."

"Go?" His confusion didn't ease, even as he stood. Sand fell from the creases in his robes, and as he straightened, his long hair swung forward. "Go ... where?"

The fox-woman only laughed.

Xiaowen frowned as he took a step closer and stopped. "You didn't answer my question."

The fox spirit grinned at him. Pointed a claw in front of them. "All right. It's to that mountain, the paifang gate at its top. You see?"

31

It was then that he saw the rolling hills of color, chiseled mountains, and at the highest peak, a great golden tree whose branches spiraled and reached high into the heavens. For a while he stood there, speechless.

Then: "Why am I here?" He turned to her. "What is this place? What—What happened to me?"

The fox-woman frowned before giving him an almost saddened look. "You don't remember?"

"No, I ... I don't." His head hurt to simply think about it. It returned him to a place of pain and rage. "I *can't*. Like I've awoken from some sort of dream. But that's not right. It's this place that has to be the dream, isn't it?"

Her ears drooped. Xiaowen flinched as she placed a palm on his cheek.

"It's okay. You'll remember when we get there." She added, "You'll be safe with me."

He removed her hand from his face. "Who are you, fox spirit?"

"I have a great many names, but you may call me Jiuwei."

=

The journey to the mountain top would take seven days.

At least, that was what Jiuwei had told him.

Xiaowen had followed her on the trampled path that curved along the coastline toward the distant hills, and much of the walk had been in silence. Instead, the crashing of the waves substituted for words.

And he noticed, though he could still feel moments pass him by, time seemed to not pass. Everything was beautiful and surreal. Floating and intangible.

I am the only real thing here.

But was he really? He was sure of so little, only certain of his name. That he had to follow this fox. That when he'd woken, he'd done so screaming in rage.

And he knew. *That* had been real.

In that brief moment between slumber and wakefulness—rage. Bloodthirst.

Real.

But that had been it.

"This is a good spot," was what the fox lady had said after they'd entered a bright and blooming forest.

Xiaowen startled out of his thoughts. They'd reached a bridge. White jade polished to a snowy white reached across and arched over to connect to a wisteria blooming cliff.

"We should rest here." Jiuwei pointed at the boulders coated in moss by the dirt path. "The bridges are harder to cross than they look, and there's no hurry for us to get to the peak."

He nodded.

And so, they sat, resting their tired legs. The constant thrum of the ocean had far receded into the horizon by now, and the sky painted in strokes of pink and yellow and orange and blue. A breeze flew by, littering petals by where they sat.

Meanwhile, Jiuwei brushed her tails hands. Fluffy, soft, and white, they swept over the rocky ground as they swayed back and forth.

She spoke. "This place is a home to many spirits. Not all of them will be as nice as me."

Xiaowen turned to face her.

She continued, "So don't stray from the path, Xiaowen. I can't guarantee that I'll save you if you do."

He gave her a curious look. He answered, "I'll try my best."

And like that, the first and second days had passed.

=

On the third day, the pair crossed over the last of the white jade bridges where they found themselves in a large clearing with hills pushing up from the ground before them. Here, the landscape turned bluish and the air clouded with a perfume-like mist.

Jiuwei fell silent, tightened her grip on Xiaowen's wrist. Her eyes darted left and right.

His brows knitted as he looked at her. "What is it?"

"You." She stopped. Restarted. "Be careful here. Please."

"Careful of what?"

"I can't say more. Just remember what I told you." She turned away, frowning. "Stick to the path. I'll be waiting."

If you pass, was what she didn't say.

With that, Jiuwei faded into the mist. Xiaowen was alone.

As he trudged along the path, figures emerged. *Statues*, he realized in horror, scattered between the ruins and broken pillars that seemed to emerge from the mist. Deep gray and rough. Yet their faces were so terrifyingly realistic. So uncanny. They all peered upwards in awestruck expressions or bowed their heads as if trying to shrink into themselves. Xiaowen's skin crawled as he passed them. *What had they seen?*

In his mind he repeated Jiuwei's words: "Stick to the path."

Carved into an archway above him were a series of illegible characters, engraved deep into the dull quartz.

"Queen" … *a queen of something. Was this once a palace?*

More and more statues emerged from the mist, whose scent of carnations and haitang blossoms grew ever more suffocating. He walked up several small stone steps, and he could see a silhouette through the fog, immense and feminine with rolling hills in the backdrop.

And suddenly, as he drew closer, he could see the figure in all its glory.

It was a statue, several gauges larger than any of the tiny human figures around him. Chiseled into the shape of a woman in robes, head fashioned with the exquisite headdress of an empress. Her eyes were closed shut as if dreaming, fingers spread across her features as she leaned into her palm. Beneath her, a fountain spewed forth the perfume-like mist. As for her lower half, however, Xiaowen now realized that what he assumed to be hills surrounding him were in fact continuations of her stone body: coils of a colossal, jade-scaled snake.

He felt as though he could spend an eternity gazing at such a beautiful woman.

Stick to the path.

That's right. The path. The path!

He hadn't strayed too far from it had he?

Just then, a chill ran up his spine. His shoulders locked instinctively. He was unsure how, but Xiaowen could tell when eyes were on him. And right now, they *were*.

He jerked and turned around to find himself staring into the foxlike eyes just inches from his own. Jiuwei's hands grabbed at his face, and nails held tight against the skin beside his eyes.

"Don't look!" Jiuwei growled, golden eyes burning with wildfire. She pulled him harder. "You'll turn into stone and become another piece in her collection. Keep your eyes on the path. You got that? Keep your eyes on *me*." She began dragging him away. "And don't look back."

And he did as she said. He ignored the eyes drilling into his back, despite his very instinct urging him to turn and face whoever dared scrutinize him so, focused on the floral patterns of the fox's robes, and ran, vaguely aware of their legs carrying them away from the snake-queen statue and her perfumed mists.

The sunlight returned and they were out of the mist.

They collapsed against a tree, panting.

Xiaowen was the first to speak. "What was that back there?"

"Baoshi-she," Jiuwei answered between breaths. "Her realm tests you on jealousy, greed, and lust. Anyone who holds these traits gets turned to stone."

He resisted his nerves' demands to look back, to ensure he hadn't been followed back to the path.

"I'm not too fond of that snake-lady. I always have to make sure she doesn't trick the ones that *do* pass into turning back. That's what happened to you."

"I'm sorry."

Jiuwei smiled at him. "Ha, it's not your fault. What's important is that you made it out. Means you have a pure soul. That's honorable."

Xiaowen frowned, mostly in an effort to hide the blood rising to his face. "I ...I wouldn't know."

The fox-woman must've taken notice of what he was thinking and laughed.

His face flushed even further and he turned away as to not look at her. "I shouldn't have said that."

"Could it be that you think I'm prettier than her?" Jiuwei giggled into her sleeve. Then came the sound of rustling silk and the little *ti-ting* of the bells in her hair.

35

Xiaowen inhaled sharply as she popped in front of his face. Her eyes were wide in a feigned innocence, ears raised high in interest.

He buried his face in his hands as he stepped back, aware of how scarlet his face had become. It did nothing to help.

"Please," he muttered.

Her laughter continued to chime with the little bells looped into her hair.

=

The fourth day, they had left behind the crumbling ruins and eerie statues.

The two of them now walked through trees that loomed gray and dry. Tough bark cracked, peeling in many places. Faces protruded from the trunks, as if trapped, dark flowers pushing out from hollow shoulders and chests. Little blue flames floated and flickered along the pathway. A few even drifted over to Xiaowen and Jiuwei, and he heard them crackle as if whispering to one another. She must have noticed him cast curious glances at them.

"They recognize you're a stranger to these lands. The wisps I mean," she explained. "They were like you, once."

Xiaowen stared at the soul-flames and suppressed a shudder. "What happened to them?"

"They became afraid and ran from the path. Into the forest, too, where the trees eventually ate them. This world is not meant for humans, so if they stray from the path and lose themselves, they'll be transformed into something that *can* belong."

He looked at them again and dug his nails into the silk of his sleeve. *They became afraid and ran from the path.*

"What lives in this forest then?" he whispered.

"You'll see."

Xiaowen huffed at that.

"After all, I don't think you'll run."

They continued in silence for several more yards, the air becoming more populated by little blue fires as they went.

Soon in their path emerged a knee-high shadow, surrounded by even more wisps. When they came closer, Xiaowen realized it was a roofed offering table, a small and simple shrine. Within it rested a stone tablet that emitted a faint glow, and engraved on its surface were characters that he could not read.

And set before it, atop the offering trays: *food.*

Fresh fruit and bowls of rice and meat. Glazed cakes and lotus crisps and hot, steamed taro buns.

Xiaowen stared. He couldn't feel hunger anymore, but the smell of the food rammed into his face like a physical blow. An inexplicable pain flooded over him. He fell to his knees in front of the shrine and watched the steam rise from the plates.

Suddenly a hand yanked at his collar.

"Wh—" Xiaowen yelled out before Jiuwei slapped a hand over his mouth.

"Shh," she shushed him.

When he managed to pry her hand from his face, Xiaowen whispered, "What are you doing? Why is there a shrine there?"

"Fourth-day's offerings," Jiuwei muttered. Her eyes focused on something ahead of them. "Not important right now. It's here. Remember. *Don't run.* I'll wait for you at the end."

With that, she was gone again.

The air had shifted. A new coldness seeped from the fog, and goosebumps ran down his spine at the sense of imminent danger.

Jiuwei. She's waiting for me at the end of the path.

Xiaowen forced his legs into motion, using the dim light of the wisps to guide himself down the path.

Then, a piercing cry. And another. It sounded like an infant. His heart seized at the sound, and his hands grew clammy.

From the fog emerged a hulking figure that towered over him by several measures. It bore resemblance to a great vulture but with the lower body of a dog with the coat of a tiger, a hunched spine, and the antler of a deer protruding from its head. And in place of its beak was the elongated mouth of an alligator, razor sharp teeth out on display. When it opened its mouth, the crying sounds of an infant rang loud into the air.

A Gudiao.

It glared at him as it slunk down the path, in his direction. Every nerve in Xiaowen's body screamed at him to run.

Don't. Don't run. Don't move. I mustn't lose myself.

His heart beat wildly in his chest as the Gudiao drew closer until it was only inches from his face. The monster circled him twice. Sniffed him. Then it gave him one last glare before it continued down the path behind him. Xiaowen watched as the creature receded back into the mist. Waited a few beats. Then broke out into a run down the path, ignoring the heavy thudding of his footsteps.

Gasping, he staggered to a halt. A familiar rush of white fur in his periphery, and Jiuwei slid into his view, all nine tails waving vigorously.

"Amazing. Most mortals never make it past that stage. They're too busy trying to run. Most people try to pass by fighting it, but you just stood still. A bit dumb of you, but you passed."

Xiaowen met her gaze and looked away just as fast. She grinned at him.

"No, really. You were great." She paused to examine him. "You're … you're okay, right? Xiaowen?"

His legs felt wobbly, threatening to collapse beneath him. He shut his eyes and breathed.

"I'm fine. It's just …"

The wind filled the silence.

"I'm dead, aren't I?"

Jiuwei suddenly seemed very interested in the grass below.

Xiaowen stared at his hands. Long fingered, thick, and callused. They felt so solid, so physical, so *real*.

"No one sees a Gudiao and lives to tell it," he said. His voice rang hollow. "But I did because I am already dead. Nothing matters. Who can I go back to, to describe how scared I was? I remember nothing. Nothing and nobody." His heart ached as he remembered the shrine. "Back there, those platters were *offered* to me, yet I have *no idea* who offered them."

"Is it really that bad?" piped up the fox-woman. "Y'know, some would kill to forget. Mortals are so full of regret. So … wouldn't it be better to leave it all behind?"

"I don't know," Xiaowen said. And that was the truth.

Her ears twitched at that.

"Maybe I ate them," she said then. "Your memories."

Jiuwei had said this with such nonchalance that for a very long time, Xiaowen stared at her. Unable to comprehend.

"I …" He grappled for words, feeling disbelief and indignation rise in his chest. "Why—why would you do that?"

The fox-spirit smiled a little. "Do you know why a fox would eat a human's heart?"

"What—"

"It's to take their memories. Emotions, specifically. It's so we can become more human—more powerful. I used to, before." She shrugged. "Not anymore, though."

Unable to suppress the anger suffocating him now, Xiaowen closed his eyes and breathed again. And by some miracle, he managed to sound eerily calm when he spoke next. "But would you still do it? If you knew what you were taking?"

"I don't know," replied the fox. "I'm not sure. But, maybe. Maybe I would."

"Why?" *Why, why?*

"Because, I'm a fox," she said as if it were an answer. "And we take memories. We eat human hearts—"

"Please stop."

"—so that we can steal their experiences for ourselves—"

"I said stop!"

She flinched, ears pinned back flat against her head. Equally startled, Xiaowen drew back and bowed his head in apology. More silence.

"I'm sorry," he said. "I shouldn't have spoken like that."

"No," said Jiuwei, and now her ears hung low, directionless.

His anger continued to subside, and Xiaowen felt a tickle of amusement; with her ears and tails, she couldn't help but wear her heart on her sleeve, could she?

"I'm sorry. I only wanted to say … losing your memories wouldn't be *so* terrible. As a mercy, of course. It just … came out wrong. I didn't mean—"

"I understand." And he really did. Even if he hated the idea of losing himself.

At that, she managed a smile and didn't add anything more. However hesitant it had been, forgiveness colored the air between them. In unspoken agreement, they sat on the earth together. Tranquil was the dead-forest around them.

Before they resumed their journey, Jiuwei spoke up.

"Long ago, I was a fox," she said. "I still am, but I wouldn't hurt a mortal. Not on purpose, not anymore." And she turned to look at him. "Not you, Xiaowen."

=

The fifth day felt peculiar.

Jiuwei led the way, and they exited the gray forest and into rolling fields and hills of shimmery bronze. Misty, still, but the sunlight had felt so odd on Jiuwei's skin.

But, no. That wasn't quite it.

Since yesterday, an awkwardness had hung about them, for reasons she could not determine.

She'd never thought much more about the mortals she'd guide to rebirth. Had led too many to remember them anymore. But this warrior man—he caught her eye and held it, so much so that it made her want to return to an earlier time, a much simpler time. A time from when she'd used to play, from when she'd been a much younger, more mortal fox.

When Jiuwei had risen to her role, she'd ascended above humans, her fox-kin, and spirits alike—became something more divine. Few ranked higher than her. And with new power came new responsibility, so she'd abandoned her mortal ways.

Now, a certain bitterness filled her mouth. She glanced back, and beneath the dreamy sun, Xiaowen's hair glinted like obsidian, long locks flowing like ink. And she thought: he was beautiful. Stunning. If they'd existed, met long, long ago, Jiuwei wouldn't hesitate to eat him alive.

Did I take his memories? She supposed it didn't matter. She didn't have the power to restore a broken soul; they had to figure it out themselves.

The Slumberer's realm was a contradiction in itself. Unlike that of Baoshi-she or the Gudiao, it was a restful, peaceful place—a strange twist upon the nightmarish circumstances by which the meadows were created. But here, spirits came to seek respite.

Jiuwei had told Xiaowen as much, and he nodded. She transformed herself into a true fox and bounded through the grass. Soft and sweet when she snapped at the stalks, the meadows were her favorite part of the path. She allowed herself to hop freely in arches, yipping while she imagined mice and miniature spirits darting beneath her paws.

Behind her, a low voice laughed. Her ears swiveled toward the sound. She turned, tails aloft, swaying.

In the sun, she could see the light reflecting off his eyes. He was smiling. Sunlit. Flesh and blood, no longer a tired, almost-ghost—but a human. She watched him like that, sitting beneath the perpetual daylight, and she became a woman again. Jiuwei brushed her robes out and went to him.

His eyes came up, and he watched her approach. "Xiaowen."

Surprise, puzzlement. And then fondness. Just a little bit. "Yes, Jiuwei?"

Jiuwei sat down close enough that their knees knocked together. Agitated, her tails swished around her. She licked her lips and swallowed all the tangled words in her throat. "I want—"

His eyes were a grayish-black. More gray than black.

Jiuwei peered into them and blurted, "I want to give you something."

Xiaowen blinked. "Oh." Then his eyes melted, and they darted sideways. "You don't have to," he murmured. "You're guiding me already. Besides, there's not much I can bring with me for long."

"I know, but—" The truth of that pulsed through her, but she continued, "But I want to. For yesterday."

Like ice, his eyes melted a little more. "Jiuwei, I have already forgiven—"

"I know," she repeated, gently. "Still. I'd like to give this to you. Will you let me?"

Xiaowen frowned, paused for a moment. But then he snapped back to sharp attention, nodded, and flipped his hand palm-up. She grinned. She hadn't even needed to convince him.

Raising a hand to her hair, she unhooked one of several golden bells tied into her white locks. Then she reached for his waistband.

Xiaowen frowned in confusion before his eyes went large. Now tied to the yaopei at the waist of his robes, the little bell hung looped at the end of the tassels of the ornament.

"There," said Jiuwei, smiling with pride at her work. "It's beautiful."

"You should know …" Xiaowen murmured. "You *are* beautiful."

You are dead, whispered something dark and weary, deep down within her. *Dead and gone, and well on your way to be reborn. And only for a little while longer will you be Xiaowen. But maybe after, I can visit the mortal world, and search, and find who you become.*

He held her hand and sighed, tender across her fingertips.

=

The sixth day, they arrived at the mountain's base. The tree towered high above, shuttering the sky in shades of gold. The path's stone stairs crawled up between its roots and vanished somewhere in the light. But there at the bottom, the lakes greeted them first.

She'd heard, the lakes were once alive and evil and spilled multitudes of black-hearted demons into the mortal and spirit realms. Now, they were just moss and metal and old, shattered stone. Most of the time.

Water lapped over the square stone steps, which were also overgrown with algae and lake-weed. Nimble as any other fox, Jiuwei hopped across. Then she stood waiting as Xiaowen carefully picked his way over, frowning as to not misstep. But every time he glanced up and caught her eyes, the corners of his mouth would quirk up before he looked down once more.

"Are you doing alright?" she called out.

"I am." He peered at the sky—an endless canopy of leaves and branches above—then back to her. "We've come so far," he said. "In much less time than I feel has really passed."

"That is how it is here," Jiuwei agreed with a shrug. "It wasn't so bad, was it?"

"No." Xiaowen let out a breathy laugh. "It could've gone much worse."

She laughed along with him and flicked her tails as she bounded across three half-submerged steps, landing perfectly on the fourth. "Run with me, if you can."

"Wicked spirit," Xiaowen chided, grinning. "You just want to see me fall into the water."

"Careful now," she said. "I may have a few tricks up my sleeve. Wouldn't want you journeying the rest of the way soaking wet."

With a sudden burst of speed, Xiaowen sprinted and sprung swift-footed across the dozen or so steps between them, such that Jiuwei reeled back to avoid him crashing into her. Except he didn't; he hopped right past her, landing on the mossy step a few feet ahead. Jiuwei stared at him open-mouthed.

"I may not remember who I was," he said with the slightest note of playfulness. "But my body recalls much more than my mind is able."

Then he *definitely* sounded amused when he added, "And it's obvious that I may have a trick or two up my own sleeves."

Jiuwei burst out into laughter again. "I never would have thought."

Xiaowen opened his mouth to reply—only to catch a breeze in his face when she sprung past as a fox on all fours once more. She could hear him shout, "Ah, that's *cheating!*" before the water began to splash as he dashed to catch up.

Jiuwei threw a glance behind; he really did run like a warrior: shoulders forward, knees bent, and crimson hair ribbons streaming in his wake.

The water grew shallower as they ran, and she could see the floor of the lake. So close to the tree's base. So close to goodbye. And yet, she didn't feel sad. How lovely.

I want to stay in this moment forever.

A sudden wind tousled her fur. Jiuwei glanced behind her and skidded to a stop.

The gate glowed. The pathway that led up to it had long been submerged by water, giving the illusion that the paifang stood directly atop the surface. Illegible engravings scratched up all around its blackened pillars, and engraved into the chipped placard right beneath the tiled roof of the gate were the characters:

長生殿

Xiaowen stood. Still as rock. Staring at it.

Jiuwei screamed.

"No!" She surged toward him, grabbed at his robes with frantic hands.

Xiaowen jumped and turned to her with huge, stunned eyes.

She shook him, shook her head with fear. "No, no! You mustn't go. Not into that one. Not that one."

For she recognized the meaning of the characters: Hall of Eternal Life.

Gates were places where souls became trapped within their own rage and hate and darkness. A number of souls which she'd guided over the course of the millennia traveled not through the tree of rebirth—but through demonic doors similar to these. They called out to mortal souls with a deep-darkness within their hearts and drew those poor, poor souls past their thresholds. From then, they returned as husks of what they once were, cursed to wander the physical and spiritual realms forever.

But this place.

The souls who entered the Hall of Eternal Life.

Jiuwei didn't know what happened to them. She could never find out. Only that they went and never came back.

And now Xiaowen.

Xiaowen.

No.

"I hear voices." His hair rippled like ink in the wind. His face was falling into itself, as if made of sand. Shock, recognition, then reignited *grief.* "They're … screaming. *Dying.* And I … I've heard them before."

"It's not real," Jiuwei pleaded, even though she *knew* the gates used nothing but truth to lure in mortal souls. "Please, Xiaowen, it isn't *real.* It doesn't matter anymore. You died. You can move on. Come, come with me to the tree. You can walk through the gate there, you can—you can be at *peace.* Please, not this, Xiaowen, not this one!"

"But," he replied to her through a daze. "I know these voices. Jiuwei, I know them. They're calling. I hear them. I can hear my sister."

Then he froze.

"My—"

She could see something in his eyes break.

"I have," he said, almost a whisper. So faint, with so much heartbreak, so much despair. "A little sister. She was—I—"

"Xiaowen," Jiuwei cried. Pulled harder at his dampened robes. "Xiaowen, Xiaowen, you're dead. You're gone. Please, don't go where I can't. Don't go where you can never return."

Because Jiuwei was the fox to be followed. The near goddess, whom the souls of mortal dead saw as their guide. She protected them on their journey and ensured that they walked through the gate into the next cycle.

But she didn't choose their gate. And she never would. It was not her role.

"I have to," he said, so softly but with so much conviction. And there, for a flash, was the face of a true, living man. A man with memories and a heart that thrummed with life.

Jiuwei despaired to see it. Hated it. For it meant that she would have to let him go.

"I have to," he spoke again, so gently. "I know why you want me to move on. But I can't willingly step into rebirth like this." He glanced back to the gate. "I woke up here so angry and empty and afraid, and I have to find out why. I have to remember what happened to me."

"You'll just forget," she whispered and felt tears running down. "But in a horrible way. You'll become something consumed by anger, and the way you died will be the *only* thing you know. You'll forget everything— even that you've lived at all—because it'll only matter how you died."

"You can't be certain of that." He brushed her tears away with cool fingertips. "I'm hurting you. I'm sorry. I hope you won't hate me, even if you can never forgive me."

"Xiaowen," she begged, again, because that had been a goodbye. "Please, don't. Don't go. Don't do this to yourself."

Jiuwei knew it had been the wrong thing to say.

Xiaowen looked at her. And he smiled. And it hurt. Hurt so much.

"But why does it matter to you? You don't even know me," he said. It seemed so much crueler for how gently he spoke the truth. "How can you, when I don't even know myself?"

Tears blurred her vision. He became a mere silhouette, then. He leaned to press his lips to her forehead. Her tails drooped limp, a few trailing in the water. Xiaowen took her face into his hands, kissed her hair again, and held her close.

"You kept me safe and treated me so kindly," he whispered. She could feel his breath puffing warm between her ears. "For that … thank you, Jiuwei."

Then he let go, and Jiuwei stumbled forward at the loss of him.

"Wait," she said. "Wait."

There was an echo of stone.

The ripple of a step onto a submerged walkway.

Then darkness, the howling of a great many winds, a *slam*—

And then.

Nothing.

And no one at all.

=

On the seventh day, a small haitang blossom floated atop the water's surface. The ripples carried it, tossed it, threatened to drown it.

Then it settled—and so did the lake. The perfect image of stillness, as if nothing ever happened.

Yet faint as air, the wind carried the sound of a fox, weeping, all alone.

TO HER

by Christine Nguyen

I will never fail to remember how I first met her.
The way her eyes smiled
And how her hair was styled
Things I could never forget.
Day after day,
Minute after minute,
My longing for her grows stronger,

My heart races as if I'm on a rollercoaster,
And then I remember
She likes roller coasters.
My heart is doing that thing again,
Beating faster,
'Til I turn into a disaster.
But I want to know more.
But she's sending me mixed signals,
Giving me mixed feelings,
And I don't know how to feel anymore,
Or what to do,
Because after all,
I just want to be with her.

Thoughts of her still race by.
Maybe I got my hopes up too high.
Even though I knew the truth,
I chose to ignore it.
Maybe it's my fault I still think of this,
Or maybe it's her.
In the end it will always be her,
Cause she's the one I want.

XI Years

by Christine Nguyen

A feeling I could never describe,
But I knew I wanted to be with you.
Certain things you did made my heart skip a beat,
Deep feelings that I only felt with you.
Every day, those memories cloud my head,
Feels like I'm going to explode,
God, I just want to be yours again.
Happiness that I took for granted.
I miss you.
Just come back.
Kiss me one more time.
Life is difficult without you.
Mornings are becoming dreadful and
Nights are becoming lonely
Our shared moments are now gone.
Pain that now aches within me,
Quality time I spent with you—now a memory.
Restless nights,
Spending my time alone,
Time passing, and the
Unconditional love I still have for you.
Vacancy within me.
Watching you move on,
XI years we've been together,
You're never coming back, but I still have
Zealous feelings left.

YOU ARE

by *Thien Nguyen*

You are the vast ocean
The endless blue sky
The warm touch of morning
And the cold kiss of night
You are the mid-autumn rain
And the early-winter snow
You are the billions of stars
That, in the dark, glow
You are the dewdrops on roses
The lovely spring showers
The sudden gale of wind
And the pink patches of flowers
You are the wish I make on dandelions
Before they blow away
You are what I long for
Each and every day

THE INK TAINTS

by An Nguyen
(Prequel to "For a Friend")

Ink, pen, and paper:
The contents that make a letter.
The girl on the bed tries to write
A letter for her friend,
For someone special.
A letter bidding goodbye
To her dearest.

Ink smudges, ink falls.
Ebony like the shining
Night sky drips from her metallic pen.

The letter falls,
descends
onto the pure white sheets,
dirtied by the smudged ink.

The glimmering pen clicks
on the marble floor.
The clean floor tainted
with ebony black ink.

A line of ink trails the letter.
From an unfinished word
to the end of the page.
Half of the message is gone.
A message never conveyed,
Undelivered confessions.

Her pale hand drops,
Gracing over the splattered ink,
Falling over the mattress.

The letter slips across the floor,
The pen flies to a wall,
tainting another material
with its grim, black ink.

The girl's body lifeless
Upon the bed.
The Grim Reaper has come,
And her soul will forever be gone
From this world.

The ink lives on.
From the tainting of the marble floor,
the splash on the wall.
the discoloring of the pure sheets.

The letter lives on,
but never complete.
Undeliverable to the receiver
without the message.

Letters need messages,
Messages need writers,
Writers need ink.

The ink can live forever,
Whether dry on a wall
Or on a sheet of paper,
but life can never be eternal.

The writer writes,
And the ink does the job
But can never finish.

FOR A FRIEND

by An Nguyen

The letters,
The envelopes—
All stored in the back
of a wooden drawer.

The ink smudged the pages,
The paper crumbled
and wrinkled

My hand glides
over the old sheets,
over the old memories
that we shared

The way we knew
every detail

The way we connected
despite never meeting.
The way we became
twin flames.

Now you are gone,
only remembered
by a mere stone,

My dearest friend,
pen pal,
and twin flame,
I wish we met sooner.

we would've been more than
a tale of two distant female friends.
We could've been more than that.
We were supposed to be
more than that.

My beloved soulmate,
I wish I'd known sooner
I wish I could've told you
"I love you."

STRINGS

by *Thomas Tran*

We were once two strings,
Together for years
Until you started to unravel.
Why?
No,
Please,
Not yet. Please, not yet.

Another week, another day,
You unravel even faster now.
Please, please!
Not yet—
I'm not ready to let you go yet.

We tried tying you back to us,
Tighter this time,
But you unraveled even faster.
Our strings tied you to us again,
But still, you unravel even faster.

One day,
The final day.
We were ready to try again,
To tie again,
But you unraveled before we could.

We begged.
We shouted
We screamed
We cried.
Not yet! Please, not yet!
Stay with us, one more day—

Just give us one more day!

I felt you smile at us.
You offered us warmth one last time.
But you felt so cold.

You tried to give us strength one last time.
But you had none left to give.

You showed us family one last time.
You are our family. Not yet. Please, not yet!

One last time
Before you finally fell apart.

I couldn't meet your eyes as you laid there.
It didn't feel right, seeing you once so full of life
Now just lying there.
But I know you must rest now
So, I swear
I'll be strong like you.

Good night, Grandfather.
Good night.
Good night.

HER ILLUSION

by Caterina Nguyen

Times she spoke to me, I saw stars in her eyes
Times she glanced at me, I heard angels in the skies
Times she touched me, I felt my heart fly

Called for her name when she had disappeared
Cried for hours after things were just as I'd feared

Struggling to find the words to describe it
Feeling like she never existed

SIX FEET UNDER

by Caterina Nguyen

You're blooming today
Under the light.
I wonder how it would feel
To always be by my side.
I feel the tension
When your cold eyes
Look into mine.

You're all I wanted
Before you changed,
All my feelings were profound.
Your sincerity was what I admired,
You told me
I was undesired.

I lay you in your place to stay,
Your chest is cold, stiff.
And you're on your back,
Arms rested on your chest,
Buried six feet under.

Goodbye, Harmonia

by Michelle Lam

THE YOUNG MAN HAD been ecstatic about the prospect of flying at the speed of light. Intelligent, charming, and beautiful–Atticus Burton was the pinnacle of perfection, the type of pilot Eisenhower wanted along with his invention in the newspaper.

"It's a wonderful opportunity," Atticus had exclaimed the month prior over a cup of coffee. He smiled, his white teeth and deep brown eyes shining under the light of the cafe.

"Well, I'm grateful that you agree," Dr. Eisenhower said, trying to hide his enthusiasm. Eisenhower liked to keep his smiles professional, his blue eyes never settled, always studying people. He thought fondly of the years he spent building the airship, along with his group of fellow colleagues and scientists. It was once only a childhood dream when young Cyrus Eisenhower wanted Belgian chocolate while he was on the other side of the world.

"I believe in looking to the future," Atticus said, "In pushing humanity forward into the horizon, into the sky. I studied in universities and flew to some places, yes, but I've never been able to make a change, you know?"

"No, I mean, I never thought so."

"I guess it feels like," Atticus glanced into his cup, stirring it, "Like people look at me and see this whole thing and think, well, he's the type of guy to be an actor for all the fame."

Dr. Eisenhower opened his mouth, but closed it, fidgeting with his clasped hands. Atticus watched him, still smiling. Even if Eisenhower didn't want to, he had to acknowledge Atticus's tall stature, shiny dark hair, and the air of charisma that he had about him. Undoubtedly, people flocked to him to admire it, and Eisenhower was no better, having sought him out for that sole purpose. Eisenhower stiffly rose from his seat.

58

"But Mr. Burton, you're taking the greatest risk for us. As a scientist and engineer, there's only so far my expertise can go. You will be making a change. Here. Now. For all of humanity," Eisenhower finally said, confident. Atticus had laughed a little, impressed, and stood up to shake his hand.

"You can just call me Atticus, Dr. Eisenhower."

In the following days, Eisenhower led Atticus through the main building, showed him the private library, research facilities, laboratories, past the lounge, kitchen, his private study, and finally, his team of scientists outside the hangar of the airship. When they turned to look at him, their white coats shifted and fluttered like the collective feathers of a colony of seagulls that caught scent of the ocean. Eisenhower briefly spared a moment for their excited introductions and pleasantries, before waving them away and hurrying Atticus into the hangar.

"Atticus, I want to introduce you to *Harmonia*, the greatest technological innovation of humankind," he said, holding out an arm, "She can fly at the speed of light, 186,000 miles per second. At 380 feet tall, she is the largest of her kind, fitted with specialized aluminum and steel. Beautiful, revolutionary, *Harmonia* is the epitome of history's dreams and desires made into reality."

Atticus's breath hitched as he stared up at the aircraft towering over them, grazing his fingers on the side of it. "She is everything you said she'd be, Doctor."

"Yes, and more. My greatest ambition, the greatest love of my life."

"I think I understand now–"

"Yes?"

"–why you never got a wife."

"You're getting ahead of yourself now, Atticus." Eisenhower shook his head, stifling his laugh with a sudden cough. A few days ago, he would've been appalled by such a comment made by any of his coworkers, much less Atticus.

"Truly, Doctor, you're exactly the kind of crazy genius I want by my side," Atticus said, turning to him, "The kind of crazy genius humanity needs to propel itself into the future."

"I wouldn't call myself crazy, but I'm glad to hear that from you. With that kind of enthusiasm, *Harmonia* is destined to succeed."

The next few weeks would be busy, with Atticus sent out on multiple practice flights at regular speeds on *Harmonia*, and Eisenhower working with his team for the final necessary observations, notes, and research. Despite that, Eisenhower found himself getting used to seeing Atticus's face every morning next to *Harmonia*, the warm sound of his voice when he greeted him, and the tinge of annoyance at his side when they bantered. Eisenhower was a master of observation and choice; he had surrounded himself with only people like him, and Atticus was nothing like him.

The day before the flight, the both of them, half asleep on the kitchen chairs, had opted to spend the rest of the night in the main building.

"You know, Doctor, I'm a firm believer of constant, positive change. I don't think that people are supposed to stay in one place; moving on is part of being human," Atticus said, resting the side of his head on the counter to face him.

"Of course," Eisenhower yawned, "I agree."

"No matter what happens, I want you to publish what happens tomorrow. Success or failure, even if they're not favorable. I'm asking you to help me, if somehow, I … well, can you do that for me, Doctor?"

"You can just call me Cyrus, Atticus," he muttered. Leaning back on his chair, Eisenhower squeezed his eyes shut and covered them with the back of his hand. He desperately wanted to sleep and ignore the ache in his throat.

On Friday, at 9:00 am, *Harmonia* shot into the air so quickly that Eisenhower and the scientists had barely caught sight of it moving before it disappeared completely.

Atticus Burton's vitals immediately began jumping and flashing violently on the screen of the control room, before going out to pitch black. Trembling with his heart pounding in his chest and ears, Eisenhower pushed the buttons for emergency recall within the same second. The screams and cries of his colleagues echoed throughout the room, desperate eyes searching through previous reports for explanations, arms flailing to reach for the radio, for countermeasures.

"Burton, come in. Burton, do you hear me?" cried one of the scientists into the radio. *How many seconds has it been?* Eisenhower racked his brain for the calculations of Atticus's distance from them, the possibilities of exploring the unknown. How long had it been since the launch? One, two, three seconds?

They recovered Atticus as soon as they could. Rushing in front of everyone, Eisenhower headed for the front of *Harmonia* before it even fully entered the port.

"Atticus. Atticus, I'm here!" he yelled out, wrenching open the door. He pulled Atticus from the driver's seat and into his arms, as close as he could to feel his pulse. It was light and slow, but it was there. Slowly, Atticus's eyes fluttered open, just enough for him to see his irises.

"Cyrus," he whispered to him, "It was beautiful." His pulse disappeared scarcely a second later, as quickly as *Harmonia* had taken to the sky.

That day, no matter where Eisenhower was in that building, the sound of sobbing and strangled gasps were audible. All of the scientists had loved Atticus Burton, accustomed to his bright figure always standing next to them, as brilliant as the stars, the sun. As far as they knew, they all murdered him.

After their daily reports, the scientists retired from the main building as soon as they could. At night, Eisenhower stood alone in the hangar, staring up at *Harmonia*.

"Doctor, you shouldn't stay here too long," a scientist said. Like the rest of them, her hair was messy from her fingers running through them countless times, her eyes glazed from crying.

"I know, thank you," Eisenhower said, without looking at her. His eyes stayed fixated on the hull of *Harmonia* and nothing else.

"Doctor, I–"

"It's fine," he interrupted, "You should go home now." Nodding, she started walking to the door, stopping once to look at him sympathetically. He never once turned to her.

Harmonia, the greatest love of his life. Since the first drawing he made as a child, he had persisted on her creation– against the doubts of countless others– and worked on her without rest, even while studying for university exams and writing books on aerodynamics. *What would Atticus have wanted?* The answer was obvious, logical, and simple. He remembered what Atticus had told him the night before.

Harmonia was beautiful, tremendous, incredible—a work of art. In order to take flight in such a form, she required a large tank of fuel. Tilting his head, Eisenhower took a lighter out of his pocket, and lit a match, watching the flame bloom. Of course, *Harmonia* was perfectly combustible.

What did it matter? You killed him, you killed him. You alone.

He dropped the match and *Harmonia* was set ablaze.

MIST

by Sonny Le

I, a lonesome wanderer,
travel through thoughts in my head
Exhaling in this mist
that calms my senses
Freezes with its touch
yet scorches me from within.

The sun visits me again,
waking me from my slumber
Now I look back,
after traveling so long,
I've finally found
my own peace.

GRAINS OF SALT

by Madison Zinnekah

There was a world long before me
With pillars of salt stretched across the sea.
Somewhere very cold,
With all stories told,
Of how beautiful we could still be.

LOVE IN WEATHER

by Teresa Le

He was the rain: dark, cloudy, storms created from his tears.
There were some who loved it, but many hated it.
When it stopped raining, everyone cheered, ignoring its beauty.
Rain was for all places; rare or every day, rain would always come.

She was the snow: pure, innocent, lovely—everything the rain was not.
Adults drank hot chocolate, watching their children play.
The sun would come out, Snow would go away, all would complain.
Everyone wished for snow, but only some could enjoy it.

Rain would be snow in freezing weather, and snow was a kind of rain.
They both were rain, but one was a ploy.
Opposites attract, they say.
Yes, they had differences, but they worked through that
For the snow loved the rain, and she would do anything to make it work.
Everyone missed them both when the weather became hot,
But hated the rain when it was not.
Nevertheless, they always enjoyed the snow,
But the biggest difference was that she could not.
Snow came annually, and the rain used the snow as a disguise to be loved.

A FOUNTAIN OF THOUGHT

by Yathy Le

A pen:
The pinnacle of creation.
Everything stems from it.

It brings life to words,
and therefore,
life to knowledge.
life to emotions.

Ink is a universal language,
One that transcends all.
From one stroke
to another,
the pen ties the threads
of the mind together.

WEIGHT OF WORDS

by Isabella Guedes

Words in Oxford Languages
Distinct meaningful elements of speech or writing
Used with others (or sometimes alone)
To form a sentence

Words to the common person
Are simply a way to communicate
To express thoughts and feelings
To connect with others

Words to me
Are waves crashing down
Like a gentle splash
Or a violent flood

From the tender age of five
I learned the weight of words
Starting with one sentence:
"You're just so exotic"

I was exotic
As in not native
As in different
As in unusual

Like being buried in sand
This enveloping feeling
Of each grain scattering across my body
Filling my lungs
Suffocating me
I choked it down
Smiling like it was a compliment

The second time I learned
The weight of words
Was when I was ten:
"I'm not mad, I'm disappointed"

You weren't mad
You weren't enraged
You weren't furious
Although I would've preferred if you were

You were disappointed
You were unsatisfied
Because I failed to fulfill your expectations
I think that hurt me more

I tried to be the best
Daughter, sister, student, friend
I held onto the rope you gave me
With the promise of being better
But your words rang in my head
Shook my body
And the rope slipped from my grip

The next time I would learn
The weight of words
Would be at fourteen:
"But you're a girl"

A girl to most people
Is pink dresses and long hair
Honeyed words and soft lips
Makeup and perfect bodies

But girls to me
Are soft, yet sharp
Some are confident
With boldness in their steps
Others are shy
Yet just as captivating in their subtlety
All are beautiful

Girls are supposed to be feminine
Girls are supposed to be nurturing
Girls are supposed to be accommodating
Girls are supposed to like boys
Girls are not supposed to like other girls
I am a girl
So why is that who I like?

BEYOND INFINITY

by Khanh Tran

"THE FIRST FLIGHT OF the *Ambassador* is about to commence in T-minus ten minutes," the P.A speakers announced. All around, scientists and engineers rushed to their appropriate stations as the launch of the spaceship *Ambassador* was about to begin.

"Showtime, Copper," one of the scientists said. Copper smirked and gave him a nod. With his helmet clenched under one arm, he strode towards the elevator which would take him to the entrance of his ship.

"Hey, Copper." A familiar voice stopped Copper in his tracks. He turned to see Dr. Boris approach him.

"Morning, Doctor. Excited for the launch?" Copper asked.

"Not as excited as you surely are." Dr. Boris looked at the monitor in the center of the room which showcased the large, white ship standing vertically. Its nose aimed at the sky. "You get to see the result of six long years of development and research firsthand."

"The whole world's watching," Copper said.

"This will be mankind's greatest achievement yet. The *Ambassador's* light-speed capabilities will allow humanity to travel the vastness of space in a short amount of time."

Copper could only smile with pride. The *Ambassador* was truly an impressive spacecraft. It showed off humanity's ingenuity in design and function and was the peak of human technological advancements. The six propulsion engines should, theoretically, allow the craft to surpass the speed of light while its reinforced titanium hull would prevent the ship from damages caused by space debris.

"Well, I won't waste your time any longer. You have an important mission after all," Dr. Boris said. He clasped Copper's shoulder. "Be proud. You're going to be the first human to travel faster than the speed of light."

Copper smiled and nodded. He gripped Dr. Boris's hand firmly as the two men said their goodbyes. "I'll see you later, Doctor."

"Get home safe, and Godspeed, pilot."

The two men parted ways and Copper continued his walk towards the elevator with his chest puffed out. He pressed the button on the elevator and was lifted to the top of the launch tower. The doors slid open and Copper took prideful strides towards the ship.

"Launch will commence in T-minus five minutes," the P.A system announced.

Copper situated himself into the cramped cockpit of the *Ambassador* and buckled up into the safety restraints. Buttons and screens blinked at his fingertips. Copper latched onto two silver bars near his sides. In front of him was a large monitor containing vital information about the spaceship along with the designated flight route.

"Copper, can you hear me?" a voice in Copper's earpiece said. He grinned at the familiar voice.

"I hear you, Doctor," Copper replied. "Everything in here seems fine and operational, ready to launch."

"Understood," Dr. Boris said. Copper looked at the timer on the top right corner of his monitor. Only a minute left until he would get launched into space and travel faster than the speed of light. He did some final pre-flight checks before the P.A system would commence the launch.

"Launching in T-minus ten, nine, eight."

Copper heard the loud engines of the spacecraft roar to life.

"Seven, six, five."

The engine grew even louder and the entire ship began to shake.

"Four, three, two."

"Good luck, Copper," Dr. Boris said.

Copper's grip on the bars tightened. He closed his eyes and took one deep breath.

"One."

Copper's body slammed back against his seat as the *Ambassador* thrust upwards from the launchpad. The altitude and speed on the screen climbed as Copper soared through the sky.

Launch successful, Copper thought to himself. The *Ambassador* left

Earth's orbit in two minutes flat. Copper was greeted with the vast darkness of space sprinkled only with the distant stars. His grip on the bars loosened as he took in the beautiful serenity of space.

"Copper, you just left orbit. It's time," Dr. Boris said.

"Got it." Despite the craft being able to exit orbit in such a short amount of time, it only displayed a fraction of the *Ambassador's* true capabilities. Copper gripped the ship's throttle and pushed it all the way forward.

The afterburner of the ship ignited and threw Copper back against his seat again. He closed his eyes as the *Ambassador* accelerated rapidly.

He opened his eyes again to see his monitors experiencing difficulties. The altitude counter was off and the speedometer climbed at a blinding pace. Copper peered around the cockpit and through the windows saw distant planets and stars whiz past him.

"Dr. Boris, can you hear me?" Copper asked. He received nothing but static. "Pilot to ground control, can anyone hear me?" Nothing. He tried slowing down the craft, but the throttle wouldn't budge.

Copper panicked. He was off course and flying too far into space. If he ran out of fuel, he would be stranded. The *Ambassador* offered no signs of slowing down. Humanity's fastest ship decided to go even faster.

Gradually, the dark void of space morphed into bright white.

He wondered if he was dead or hallucinating. His breathing became labored and he struggled to keep his eyes open. He faded in and out of consciousness as the blinding light engulfed the entire cockpit.

Copper squeezed his eyes shut and drew in one long breath before he passed out.

It wasn't until the entire hull started to shake that Copper was brought back into consciousness. He rubbed his eyes and tried to get his bearings. He looked out into space before his face paled. The *Ambassador* was rapidly accelerating towards a planet.

"Unknown spacecraft, identify yourself," a voice said in Copper's communicator. Her voice stirred something inside Copper. It was hope. Hope that he could be saved from this flying tomb. "You're coming in too fast. Decrease your speed."

The voice spoke English. Did his ship somehow make it back to

Earth? Was it ground control? If it was, how could his spacecraft be unknown?

Copper tried to respond, unable to hide his excitement at the promise of making it home. "This is the *Ambassador* to ground control. Can you hear me?"

There was silence. Copper assumed it was just radio interference and decided to shift his attention to the monitor. The speedometer seemed functional again. He gripped the ship's throttle and pulled back to decrease the speed. The *Ambassador* re-entered the atmosphere.

"May I ask who I am speaking to?" the voice on the communicator said.

"This is Pilot Copper of the *Ambassador*. I just entered Earth's atmosphere and I'm about to crash land," Copper replied.

"Earth? This isn't Earth."

Confusion immediately settled in. He looked at the map on the monitor before he grimaced. The map wasn't working, broken from the *Ambassador*'s extreme speed.

"Then where—" Before Copper could finish his question, he launched forward from his seat as the *Ambassador* crash-landed onto the planet surface, his harness kept him from flying across the cockpit. The monitor turned black, and the floor rumbled.

A few seconds passed until the *Ambassador* ceased its movement.

"Copper? Copper, are you alright?" The voice asked.

"Yeah, I'm fine. I think. No injuries," Copper said, although his rib started to ache from the harness.

"Thank God, we thought we lost you again. You just crash-landed."

"I can see that." Copper went to the emergency door of the ship. "And what do you mean again?"

"You and the *Ambassador* have been missing for over sixty years."

Before Copper opened the door, he paused. "Sixty years? No, no. That's impossible. I don't believe you."

"Believe what you want, but you're not on Earth."

"Then where am I?" Copper opened the door and stepped out to see what looked to be a rainforest. He noticed the impossibly high waterfalls which seemed to stretch all the way to the sky. The steam caused by the

73

falls created a warm, comforting atmosphere akin to a hot spring. The plant life and colors were of a mixed rainbow palette, and creatures Copper had never seen before flew above the sky.

"Copper, this is Augustina." The voice said as the pilot's eyes widened. "Earth's twentieth outer space colony."

GOODBYE LETTER STUCK TO THE FRIDGE

by Kellan Nguyen

here's a truth i've never told anyone:
i don't know what love is.

you'd think i would, but i don't.
a simple truth i've known my whole life.

eighteen years ago,
cradled in my mother's arms,
made of love: and yet,
i could not feel it.

love curled along the sides of the house,
embedded in all my fairy lights and yet,
i still didn't feel it.
i didn't feel anything.

there must've been a time when i did.
or i'm just telling myself that
so my hands won't shake and
my skin won't melt off my bones.

maybe there were days shining
like morning dew on leaves,
days when i didn't feel so alone.
maybe i felt love in those summers
of honeysuckle and laughter,
or maybe i didn't,

but i do know i've grown tired of this idleness,
and i'm not sure how much farther the oasis is,
if it even exists at all,
if i'm going to wilt before i make it out.

i want to feel a longing so deep it etches itself
into my bones, a light so bright it hurts me.
i want to lie beneath stormy clouds and bathe myself
in the rainstorm's humming,
or i'd step back inside, watching solemnly
and praying my own thunderstorms
stop cracking open my insides.

i want to be the fuzz of the peach on the kitchen counter,
i want to be the neatly folded silk
tucked away in my mother's old dresser,
i want to be the beat of a hummingbird's wings,
because soft things are always loved,
and it would be nice, i think, to feel that way.

i've never been a vivid gladiolus in a field,
nor have i ever been a picturesque landscape,
the steady crescendo of ocean waves,
or a full moon in the night sky;
i'm just a child, and all i long for is to feel something.

my record player, my figurine collection,
the home i've built in this town: i'd give it all,
and maybe, just maybe,
it would be enough to stave off this hunger.

i'll give my friday nights, my saturday mornings,
my sunday afternoons. i'd pack up and leave,
and i have done so by the time you're reading this.

i would go to a city on the other side of the country, perhaps,

because i never grow tired of seeing those lights,
or i could be in the countryside
because i've always enjoyed seeing the stars so much more.

anywhere would be fine,
because i just want to find a place
where my hands feel like my own
and my bones actually fit together
and there is no more lead weighing me down like a plague.

i would find love in every cup of coffee
i brew under the morning sun
and in the succulents living on the windowsill
and in a soft crook of the couch and
everything, everything, everything.

i want to live, and someday,
i'll tell myself "this is love,"
and i would be right.

DARKNESS

by Laura Miranda

The very meaning of darkness is wickedness;
Fear and hopelessness.
A poison surrounds a pure heart,
Slowly dyeing it black
At the end of every tunnel, there is light
But there is no light here.

Wanting to wake up,
Feeling like the air has been sucked out of your lungs,
Trying to breathe,
Knowing that there is nothing left,
Only darkness.

No light at the end
Just the darkness to keep you company
No faith, no hope
Just the heart turned cold and black.

LIES

by Laura Miranda

Every day she would ask for a hug
And every time he would nod and shrug
He would never treat her wrong
And they would always get along
Their laughter and their talks
Hide that their hearts are still locked.

SUNKISSED

by Bethanie Luu

Fiery and passionate
Warm and kind,
Soft rays that trace
Murmuring strokes
Across velvet petals,
Leaving me
Breathless,
Sunkissed.

I LOVE YOU THAT MUCH

by Hillary Nguyen

I love you so much
That even though
I love chocolates
And I'd hoard them
if anyone else asked,
I'd give them all to you.
That even though
I'm a nightmare in the kitchen,
I'd make your favorite food
Which, thank God, is just a fruit salad
(Even if I'm 90% sure you just said that
So, I wouldn't burn the house down)

I love you so much
That even though
We're both imperfect messes
And there are times
Natural disasters occur
When we fight and our storms collide
And your words tear my insides
And make me want to cry,
I'll still stay by your side
Even though it's terrifying
To know that there's someone
Who believes in me so much,
Who also feels the same,
I love you that much.

LOVE LETTER TO THE FOOL

by Stella Nguyen

Always there for me
Boy, is he a sight
Can he be any more perfect?
Doesn't know how beautiful he is,
Even though he has his flaws
Fluffy hair, soft like silk,
Green, trademark sweater
How is he so gorgeous?
Inky black hair
Just me yearning for him
Knowing that he's on my mind
Lucky to share this world
More days I want to spend with you
Not enough words to describe my euphoria
Over the moon every time you smile
Please be the king to my queen
Quests I shall embark for your love
Rosy red cheeks when you're near
Searing passion from within
Take my heart and feel what I feel
Under the stars, I'd love to kiss you
Very much in love
Want to be together soon
XOXO, hugs and kisses
You are special to me
Zestful our love shall always be

WAVES OF INDIGO
by Bethanie Luu

THE MERMAID COMES OUT of nowhere. *Concealed,* Zachary notes; beneath the sun, the sea shimmers clear and blue like sapphire crystals, and the sun shoots through the waves with searingly bright rays. But here in the night, the sea and sky complement each other in shades of near-black indigo and deep purples, the complete darkness giving the ocean an illusion of a vast pool of inky salt-water.

The rowboat drifts. In silence, only the sound of water prevails. No light shines more than what is provided by the moon.

Having spent over half a decade on the run had taught Zachary to watch for movement in the shadows.

A rolling motion amidst the current around him and an oddly soft splash catch his attention. And so, he looks.

And there it is.

The same dark, gleaming shade as the rest of the night-sea. Elongated fins fan out from both sides of its head. Its body, adorned with fish hooks and netting and silver line, tarnished rings and bits of barnacle. Its hair, white in mimicry of foam. Its eyes aglow in strange violet.

It fixes on Zachary at once; it has no pupils. Even so, the mermaid is beautiful, ethereal, and very unnerving to look upon.

"Ah." It takes him a moment to make an actual sound, tongue thick in his mouth – dried out and awkward. "Hello."

The mermaid says nothing. The water behind it ripples. Long, coils of shadow twisting and arching and threatening to break through the ocean's surface.

What would a mermaid's tail feel like against the hardened skin of his hands? A fish? Or more like an eel: slippery, thick, and smooth?

Don't touch mermaids, Zachary, an old warning pierces his mind. *Never, ever, ever touch a mermaid. Beautiful as they are, they are cruel and ruthless.*

He stares at his palm. Flexes his fingers. Drops them back into his lap.

"I figure you're here to eat me?" Zachary asks, tired.

Ever so slowly, the mermaid breathes out. Seawater pours from its nostrils and bioluminescent eyes. It blinks for the first time. Little spots of color splash over the mermaid's indigo nose and cheeks in a strange likeness to freckles. Zachary thinks, if it had stayed under water, he would have never seen it at all. He would have mistaken it for the reflection of stars twinkling over the sea or glimpses of jellyfish far, far below.

It would have overturned the boat and dragged him deep beneath the waves before he ever knew what happened.

"Well," Zachary rasps. "I wouldn't make a good meal, I don't think. Thin and stringy, you see."

"Are you dying?" The mermaid's voice is and isn't what he expected. Rather than chilling and eerie, it is soft, indifferent, and vaguely accented, though inhuman in its own way. It is water licking against a rowboat's side, piercing cold through his heart.

"Not yet. But soon, I suppose." Zachary offers a pallid smile, rueful. He explains, "I've run out of fresh water two days ago, and I've half a day of food left. And it's been horribly sunny."

He receives no response, and the mermaid continues to stare at him with its cool, mirror-smooth expression. Water drips down its chin, down across dark lips – soft despite the saltwater.

Thoughts fraying, Zachary thinks with the idleness that spawns of severe dehydration. His sister had always said she wished to kiss a mermaid. What a temper she'd throw if she knew he had come closer in the end.

"Would you like it? It's only a bit of salted fish." His fingers dangle over the edge of the rowboat. "I don't know if it'd be very appetizing to you, but since I have no more water, well. It won't be doing me any good."

Darkness oozes and ebbs, and there is salt crusted in his nose, in the corners of his eyes, and his limp, greasy hair. His grip is weak, and so the little paper package slips from between his fingers. But he doesn't hear it hit the water. Instead, he watches the mermaid duck below. When it reemerges, he could see the fish's tail poking out of its mouth, impossibly sharp and pointed teeth clamping down on it.

"Ah." Zachary says. He now realizes that the mermaid had taken the fish from his hand. Again, he flexes his fingers but now tries to recall if he had even felt it, the brush of wet skin against dry.

He ignores the abrupt surge of longing in him.

The mermaid swallows it whole, and for a second, Zachary gets the disturbing sight of its throat expanding the same way a snake's does when devouring prey. But the instant passes, and the mermaid is eerily lovely again, an inky silhouette as it swims to the edge of the rowboat. It reaches a hand out of the water. Curls it over the boat's edge.

Zachary cannot help but draw back when the mermaid pulls itself up for a closer look at him. Its fingers are a joint too long. It has no fingernails. Instead, its hands end in black, hard talons as though the digits themselves were bone or coral, sharpened to points. The mermaid's eyes cast a dim, violet phosphorescence over the creaking wood boat.

"I," it says in that soft, enthralling voice, "could save you, if you'd like."

Blue and silver and purple freckles—the same as those adorning its face – scatter and glimmer across the mermaid's collarbones, over the smooth curves of its shoulders. Zachary casts a glance at its chest, just barely above the oily sea-surface. Flat in resemblance to a male humanoid—devoid of nipples or navel.

"Oh," Zachary says. He doesn't need to force a bark of laughter. "You have no idea what I've done. I don't even know if I'd be worth saving, to be honest with you."

The temptation to touch—to feel, to slide, to explore wet ocean-skin with a fingertip, with his wide-open palms – now begins to burn within his bones. Zachary clenches his hands into fists, shoving them against his shriveled, aching belly in order to not reach out toward this frighteningly alluring sea-dark creature.

That's their enticement, rings a memory of an old story. *Their charm, you see. Merpeople don't often need to hurt you on their own. It's the way you'll happily choose to jump into the water with them that gets you killed.*

"No?" whispers the mermaid. Its hand uncurls from the boat's rim. Stretches forward. Reaches for him. And Zachary, ah. Zachary has no more room to get away.

The hand is wet, dripping salty water onto the bottom of the boat. But the mermaid doesn't touch him, instead tapping a long, talon against the locket that rests around his neck. Tap-tap, and the shape of the metal thuds twice against Zachary's chest like an external heartbeat.

Nothing more happens. The sun doesn't rise; the air is salty and stale. No one else will gaze upon this scene but the half-crescent moon and the wispy clouds above.

"I am curious," the mermaid says. "About your world, about your kind. About the despair that bleeds into the water around your boat because you are dying. And so, the force within you cries out for salvation, uncaring of who answers. I have always been curious. Will you provide me with the answers I seek to learn?"

Zachary's heart is pounding. He swallows and there is no saliva.

"Is it true," he manages, "that if you touch a mermaid with your bare hands, you'll never be able to let go, even as they pull you underwater to drown?"

The mermaid smiles. Zachary feels the sight of it catch in his throat. Like a noose around his neck, like water pouring into his lungs. Like a fishing hook.

"You are suspicious," murmurs the mermaid, an ocean-song voice, "but curious as well – something I like. My answer shall depend. How badly do you want to find out? Or rather–" Another fish-hook smile. "How badly do you wish to learn?"

It begins to draw its arm back. Zachary makes a split-second decision and catches its arm between both his hands.

He ignores the coldness of the skin and the hooked points of talons frigid against his flesh.

He says, "Very much."

The talon fingers curl – first very gently, then crushing very, very tightly – around his.

Zachary whispers, "I want that, very much so," and waits for the pull.

86

MECHANICAL HEART

by Yathy Le

If you were to ask me
what lies within my heart,
I would not know.

Even now
As you tear me apart for your work
I still would not know

Amongst the mechanical
ticks of my brain,
and the billions
of 0's and 1's,
I'm sure you'll find your
answer somewhere.

Tear off my skin,
Grind my bones.
Strip me of my everything in
your pursuit of knowledge.

Are you satisfied?
Have I answered your question?
Then, tell me,
with your bloodstained hands,
tell me the song of my soul.

ONE SHARED PLACE

by Christine Nguyen

One shared place,
Oh, how mysterious life is.
The never-ending cycle
Different people, stories, and experiences.
All with issues not shown to the public eye,
Masking and hiding,
Not knowing what's behind.
We wear them for the sake of surviving.
Just like how the bartender works
To support himself and his family,
Barely getting by,
Living check after check.
Or the couple who fights every night,
But stay together for the sake of their "family"
Despite not feeling the same kind of love,
Constantly wishing they never met.
And the man who sits alone,
Drained down to the bone,
Wishing his time would fly right by.
They all meet in one place,
Where nobody knows who is who
And everybody's issues are gone.
They share in the moment
And sip their drinks
Distracted from the pain.

Icarus' Fall

by Andy Nguyen

Daedalus once had an apprentice,
whose skill rising faster was horrendous.
So, he pushed Perdix off a cliff in a fit of rage,
Nearly got himself locked away in a cage.

Daedalus was forced to take refuge in Crete.
After nearly killing Perdix, he had to be discreet.
Athena turned Perdix into a bird
and Daedalus left Athens without a word.

King Minos had Daedalus build a maze,
so confusing that it would leave anyone in a daze.
Minos tried to hide the Minotaur's existence
by locking in a tower Daedalus and Icarus.

Daedalus, the genius inventor,
made two pairs of wings of splendor.
Using only wax and feather,
they planned to escape together.

He told his son not to fly too high,
or his wings would burn and he would die.
Icarus did not listen and in less than an hour,
he was overcome by his newfound power.

HERO'S ROLE

by Hillary Nguyen

CHARACTERS

NARRATOR
ERVAR, The Hero
LUIS, The Demon Lord
SERVANT, Luis' servant

SETTING

Ervar's house. The room is cramped with fabric and sewing materials everywhere.

SCENE I

ERVAR is sitting in his room, using a sewing machine. He hears a noise.

ERVAR. What was that?
NARRATOR. The young man turned his head, looking for the sound of the mysterious noise.
ERVAR. Who said that?
NARRATOR. He still could not find the source of the sound so he went to the front door.

(ERVAR opens the front door. There is a sword lying on the ground)

NARRATOR. He had been chosen by the Holy Sword. Now a hero, he must take up the sword and–

(ERVAR shuts the door and returns to his seat)

NARRATOR. W—wait, what are you doing?

ERVAR. Not listening to you. I need to finish sewing.

NARRATOR. You can hear me? Wait, no, stop. Stop sewing, take that sword, and go defeat the Demon Lord.

ERVAR. No thanks, I'm busy right now.

NARRATOR. That wasn't an offer!

(ERVAR ignores NARRATOR and keeps sewing)

NARRATOR. To keep sewing, you're going to need money. And if you want more money, just go defeat the Demon Lord and steal his treasure. He has thousands of gold coins.

ERVAR. I guess I do need more money but being a hero doesn't sound like a fun job.

NARRATOR. It's fun! Very fun and rewarding. So, hurry up and go fight the Demon Lord already.

ERVAR. Ok, but I'm going to look for other job openings, too.

NARRATOR. Wait, why? You're the hero. what else would you do?

.

SCENE II

Later that day in the afternoon. The countryside with sloping, green hills. ERVAR is laying down, staring at the sky leisurely. The sword is on the ground nearby.

NARRATOR. You've been staring into the sky for half an hour. Can you go now? Come on, up and at 'em.

ERVAR. Why the rush? It's a perfectly good day to just enjoy the scenery.

NARRATOR. It's a perfectly good day to vanquish the Demon Lord.

ERVAR. What do you have against the Demon Lord? Did they murder your family or something? Destroy your village?

NARRATOR. I'm trying to make a story here. Can you just play your part?

ERVAR. I already said I'm not interested. Why do you keep telling me what to do?

NARRATOR. Listen, I'm the narrator. I make the rules. You're the hero. You have the Holy Sword and you're going to use that sword on the Demon Lord. Come on, this is as easy as saying that tomatoes are vegetables.

ERVAR. No, everything you said was wrong, especially tomatoes. Tomatoes are fruits.

NARRATOR. No, they're not. They're vegetables.

ERVAR. Fruits have seeds and grow from the flower of that plant. Tomatoes have seeds and grow from the flower of the plant. So, tomatoes are fruits.

NARRATOR. That's a terrible definition. That means cucumbers are fruits too.

ERVAR. Yeah, cucumbers are fruits.

NARRATOR. No, they're not! Wait you know what, fine. Let's pretend tomatoes are fruits. But if they're fruits, how come they're in salads with other vegetables? No one puts tomatoes in a fruit salad.

ERVAR. You're categorizing tomatoes by what they're surrounded by. We shouldn't be defining something based on its situation. Tomatoes should be defined individually due to individual characteristics, which are seeds, meaning they're fruits.

NARRATOR. I'm not talking to you anymore. Clearly, you can't listen to reason.

ERVAR. Fine by me. Your voice was getting annoying anyways.

NARRATOR. Why, you–

ERVAR. Didn't you say you weren't talking to me anymore?

(NARRATOR stammers in frustration. ERVAR ignores NARRATOR'S voice and continues staring into the distance. SERVANT enters and rolls a red carpet onto the grass. LUIS enters, walking on carpet.)

LUIS. Oh hello, didn't see you there.

ERVAR. Are those horns on your head?

LUIS. Oh these? Yes, they are. I'm a demon, after all.

ERVAR. Huh, a demon. First time I'm meeting one.

LUIS. That's not surprising. We usually keep to ourselves so humans don't find some reason to attack us.

ERVAR. So, what do you demons usually do?

LUIS. Hmm, probably the same things your village does. Hunt for meat, look for berries and herbs, harvest crops, clean the house, do laundry. Day-to-day stuff. The commoners anyways.

ERVAR. Yeah, that sounds really normal. Can't imagine why anyone would want to kill you.

LUIS. I sure hope not, since we've worked so hard just to get a peace treaty with your king.

ERVAR. Didn't hear about that. I really should leave my house more.

LUIS. What do you do at home that keeps you from hearing this kind of common news?

ERVAR. Oh, sewing. I make my own clothes and patch up my neighbors' clothes when they ask. They say that my embroidery is pretty flashy though.

LUIS. You make your own clothes? They look really nice, I thought you must have ordered them from a tailor. Actually, would you like a job as my personal tailor?

ERVAR. Personal tailor?

LUIS. Yes, making clothes for me. I could really use someone like you. My castle is actually nearby so why don't we go there and discuss the details?

ERVAR. Wait, are you the Demon Lord?

LUIS. Indeed, I am. Now are you coming or not? Also, is that your sword on the ground?

ERVAR. Oh, I was just holding onto that for someone. They don't need it anymore so I think I'll just sell it.

NARRATOR. What– no, that's the Holy Sword! The most valuable weapon in the land! Don't just sell it like it's something of little importance!

LUIS. Did you hear a voice or was that just me?

ERVAR. It's fine, just ignore it. Anyways, the job sounds interesting, so mind leading the way to your castle?

LUIS. Yes, of course. Naturally, I'll give you a fair salary and paid vacation.

SERVANT. Uh, pardon my intrusion, Your Highness, but can I have a paid vacation too?

LUIS. Of course not. You're a servant. Keep working.

(SERVANT scrambles to roll carpet all the way to the other side of the stage. There are tears streaming down his face as he leaves the stage.)

ERVAR. So, tell me more about the job.

(ERVAR, sword hanging by his side, and LUIS walk offstage)

NARRATOR. What kind of development is this?

SCENE III

Afternoon inside LUIS's castle. LUIS and ERVAR walk in.

LUIS. So that's everything. Do you accept?

(SERVANT hastily brings out a throne, which LUIS sits on. ERVAR steps in front of him)

ERVAR. It sounds amazing, though I'd like some time to think it over.

LUIS. What would you possibly need to think about? Hundreds of people would be thrilled to be in your position.

ERVAR. Yeah, I guess.

LUIS. So, you agree! Splendid! My servant will lead you to your new quarters.

ERVAR. What—no, this is way too sudden. Weren't you listening? I need some time.

LUIS. You'll have all the time you want here.

NARRATOR. Ervar inhaled and murmured under his breath.

ERVAR. Do I really have to deal with another bloke who can't listen? (sighs) But it's not like I can just leave.

NARRATOR. Another? Did you just lump me in with him?

LUIS. What was that?

ERVAR. Nothing.

LUIS. I could've sworn I heard someone talking about me. They must be praising me.

ERVAR. Right. Of course, that's the case.

(LUIS taps his chin with a finger.)

LUIS. You know, talking with you has made me realize that there are so many people out there who don't know who I am. Their lives are unfulfilled and yet they don't even know.

ERVAR. Yeah, truly a shame that not everyone in the entire world has to listen to you drone on about yourself.

LUIS. So true You really do understand me. I didn't want to start a war because it'd be such a hassle but maybe I should conquer the world, if only for everyone to know my name and gaze upon me. Here's your first job. Make an outfit for my debut as I get ready to conquer the continent. Small steps first.

ERVAR. Wait, an actual war? I don't think I can support that.

LUIS. Right, too much work. Well then, let's start a business. Open up tailor stores across the continent. I might as well milk money out of everyone. If I can't conquer their kingdoms, then I'll conquer their livelihoods.

ERVAR. Alright, that I can do.

NARRATOR. What kind of hero are you? That's not what the hero should be saying. Where's the Sword? Come on, defeat the Demon Lord before he embarks on his quest of world domination.

ERVAR. I mean, he's not going to start an actual war so it should be fine. Also, I told you, I'm selling the sword.

LUIS. It does look quite expensive. Should be a decent contribution to our starting capital—genius idea if I do say so myself.

NARRATOR. No, no, no. This is not how the story is supposed to go.

LUIS. Let's discuss more in my conference room.

ERVAR. Ok, let's go.

(ERVAR and LUIS walk off stage. the lights dim. NARRATOR sighs in resignation.)

NARRATOR. I think I'll just narrate a horror story instead. Should be easier. They all die in the end anyways.

THE END

LIGHT ALL OVER

by Vincent Quach

Sun shines from above,
Lighting up the world below.
It then becomes bright.

GREEN BELOW AND ABOVE

by Vincent Quach

Green all around you,
Down to the soft stalks of grass
And the tall tree leaves.

THE RETURN OF THE SUN

by Sydney Dao

The sun rising slow
Rabbits coming out to play
Spring arriving soon

WINTER'S GALAXY

by Sydney Dao

Snow taking over
Nighttime coming earlier
White snowflakes like stars

MELODY OF A HEARTBEAT

by Sydney Dao

A symphonic voice
The orchestral rings and strings
My heart sings with joy

SPRING

by Teresa Le

Winter is long gone
The snow melts, the flowers bloom
Rid Winter, greet Spring

WIND

by Teresa Le

Gentle is the breeze
A puff of indignant air
Flowing through nature

SUMMER

by Teresa Le

The hot air blows through
Where the spring air once traveled
Summer, nature's fire

ART OF MIREK KUZNIAR

by Alham Attaee

If you were a poem, how would you paint me?
If you were an artist, how would you paint me?
If you were the sun, how would you paint me?
If you were the moon, how would you paint me?
If you were the clouds, how would you paint me?
If you were the dirty alleys, how would you paint me?
If you were the clean streets, how would you paint me?
If you were Mirek Kuzniar, this is how you would paint me.

If it wasn't for the towering trees, I wouldn't be complete
If it wasn't for the rushing cars, I wouldn't be complete
If it wasn't for these shining lights, I wouldn't be complete
If it wasn't for these bright colors, I wouldn't be complete
If it wasn't for these grand buildings, I wouldn't be complete
If it wasn't for the lovely blue ocean next to me, I wouldn't be complete
If it wasn't for Mirek Kuzniar, I wouldn't be complete.

TROUBLE ABOVE THE SURFACE

by Vincent Quach

SUMMER BREAK WAS HERE, and Hanh could hardly contain her excitement.
Two years of college down, two more to go. Finals were finally done.

She and a few of her classmates planned a party on the sea to
celebrate surviving the first two years of college. Her friend Beth had
managed to get her hands on her family's old sailboat and took everyone
out off the coast of the Pacific. Hanh admired the view as they were out to
sea and leaned against the rail. What a view.

The vessel jerked sharply to one side. She grabbed the railing, nearly
falling overboard.

"You alright?" Beth asked.

"I'm fine." Hanh peered over the side. "But the water's getting a little
rough. Maybe we should go somewhere else?"

Beth took a peek over the boat. "It's not that bad. You worry too much."

Hanh was a little skeptical—the boat rocked back and forth with the rough
waves which sloshed against the sides and sprayed water up on the deck.
But, well, if Beth thought it was fine…

Even anchored, the water was still choppy and the boat swayed. Hanh
looked around. Did anyone else care? They were busy pulling out soda
from the coolers, eating snacks, and turning up the music. Everyone was
having a good time, and before she knew it, Hanh had forgotten about her
worries and gone along dancing with the others, or at least trying to while
knocking against the cabin walls.

Hanh stumbled again and grabbed a hold of the railing. The currents
were getting rougher, and she looked back at Beth and at the other people
laughing as they swayed back and forth on the deck.

"Beth, the boat," Hanh called out, but no one could hear her over the
pounding bass of the songs.

Hanh stepped forward but was shoved into the railing by a sudden

100

listing towards the starboard side. Another, another, and another, and then with one final list, a huge wave smacked against the side.

Hanh grabbed at the railing but missed, falling overboard. Nobody seemed to notice.

She flailed in the waves, struggling to keep her head up above the water, but every time, the waves pushed her back under. Unable to breathe, she began to feel dizzy, a sharp pain in her ears and her eyes, her limbs heavy with fatigue.

Everything went black and her lungs burned.

Hanh woke up on a shoreline, her vision blurred, sick to her stomach, and her body feeling like it was still floating on the sea.

Was she dreaming? And if she were, who was that ... the woman pressing on her chest?

With a final compression, Hanh coughed out the last of the water from her lungs. Before she could say anything, the woman dived back into the ocean.

"Wait!" Hanh sprang up.

The woman had already disappeared beneath the waves.

Hanh thought that she caught a glimpse of a fish tail. But, no. That wasn't possible, was it?

Hanh wasn't sure if she was hallucinating, but whatever she saw was gone now and she was alone on a beach she'd never been on before. She scanned the horizon. The sailboat was nowhere to be seen. Did anyone know where she was? How was she going to get back?

She turned onto her side and stuck her finger in the sand and started a little spiral. She just needed a bit of hope to get back alive. To college. To Beth.

Something splashed up to shore. She looked up in disbelief.

That couldn't be real, that just couldn't. Maybe she was in the water for too long, and... the hallucination would just go away and she'd be all alone again.

Hanh crawled closer to the water.

There in front of her was a mermaid with black hair, a vibrant orange and yellow tail at the end of her body, looking at her face to face.

Hanh didn't dare get closer, not to something like her, something so similar yet so mythical. She could see in the mermaid's eyes that she likely felt the same.

There was only the crash of waves, the same waves that stole Hanh, as both of them gazed at each other in silence.

"Hello." Hanh waved.

The mermaid blinked. "Hi. I'm Chau."

That thing ... well, person—mermaid was real. And now it was talking to her.

"I'm ... I'm Hanh," she said. "Thank you for saving me."

Chau smiled and swam towards her. The two chatted for a while as they waited for Hanh to be rescued.

"I've heard a lot of stories of you mermaids, though they're usually with pink or red hair. You seem a little different from what I've heard," Hanh said.

Chau chuckled. "Well, our community is more diverse than you think. We're all from different parts of the ocean. I'm from the Eastern Sea, in the Pacific."

"How do you breathe on land and underwater?"

"I have gills for breathing underwater and a nose and lungs for land," Chau said.

Hanh began to ask more questions. They spoke, laughed, and shared stories for hours. Despite their obvious differences, they shared much in common.

The sun set further beneath the horizon.

"Meeting you has been great." Chau sighed and looked at the golden light across the sea. "But I wish we could see each other more after this."

"Actually ..." Hanh closed her eyes, thinking. "There's a pier near Cross Country beach. I've never seen anyone there even in the day, so we can just meet at the beach near there at night. Think that'll work?"

"That sounds great. Just promise me you won't tell anyone about this," Chau said.

"Why?"

Chau sighed. "I don't want any more of us to be hunted."

Hanh was about to ask what Chau meant, but then the sound of a propeller filled the air. Off in the distance, a helicopter's searchlight panned over the water.

Without another word, Chau immediately dived back into the water, just in time for the searchlight to find Hanh.

Soon after, a coast guard boat arrived and picked up Hanh and, an hour later, reunited her with her friends. As her friends hugged her, she couldn't help but wonder what Chau meant by "more of us to be hunted."

At home, Hanh wondered if people had discovered mermaids before and kept their discovery a secret. Her friend Leah, however, couldn't help but notice Hanh had been quiet and she furrowed her brow.

"Hey, is something wrong?" Leah asked.

Hanh didn't respond.

Leah called her again and again before tapping her shoulders, snapping her out of her thoughts.

"Oh, I'm fine. I'm just a bit out of it. You know, nearly drowning and all," she responded.

Leah frowned. "You sure you don't want to talk about it?"

"I'm fine."

Leah could see Hanh was getting antsy and backed off.

When Leah left the room, Hanh felt a twinge of guilt, but she had a feeling something was off. She wasn't planning on carelessly giving away information until she knew what made Chau so nervous on that beach.

After her friend went to sleep, Hanh snuck out of the house and drove to the pier to see if Chau would be there.

When she arrived, she walked to the edge of the pier to wait for Chau to arrive. As she waited, she heard something back on the beach where she saw two men on the sand near a pickup truck. One pulled open the tailgate while the other dragged a squirming body from the shore. As Hanh watched, she saw moonlight reflecting off of the lower body—no, a tail—before the men threw the person into the back of the pickup truck, pulled a cover down, shut the tailgate, and drove off. Hanh gaped after them. Did they just kidnap a mermaid? What if that was Chau?

Hanh ran back to her car and followed them. The streets were empty that night, so she caught up and followed their truck from a distance. They didn't go too far before turning into an empty lot near the docks beyond the pier.

Hanh kept driving until the lot was out of sight. She parked and walked back to the lot, which was scattered with boats, ready to be launched from the nearby docks. Looking further around, she spotted some light from a fishing shack and headed towards it.

She moved around a couple boxes and got close enough to peek into the window, and as she suspected, the men truly did kidnap a mermaid, but it wasn't Chau. The mermaid, with a yellow and red tail was tied up and gagged.

One of the men walked towards the mermaid with an electric saw.

Hanh watched in horror as one man cut her tail off while the second shaved her head.

"I told you mermaid merchandise is in demand," one of the men said. "Whoever thought people would pay huge bucks for these tails and wigs?"

"Yeah, yeah, I get it. Shut up and finish cutting."

Hanh held back a cough, about to vomit, but covered her mouth, hands shaking. What was she watching?

After the men collected the tail and hair, they picked up what was left of the mermaid.

"Right, let's just toss it back into the ocean."

Swallowing her bile, Hanh scrambled away to hide, tripping over a couple of boxes in her hurry. Hearing the noise, one of the men threw the door open and Hanh ran faster.

"Hey!" one of the men shouted.

"Grab her!" another yelled as he loaded his gun.

Hanh sprinted as fast as she could back toward the pier. She heard gunshots behind her. The men were getting closer and closer.

Hanh was at the edge of the pier with the men right behind her. She bit her lip and jumped into the water. She gasped as the sudden cold froze her nerves. She kicked and swam up to the surface.

Her head broke through the water, just in time to hear a bullet shoot past her. She looked up to see one of the men about to pull the trigger again.

A force yanked her underwater.

One of the men cursed overhead.

The other patted his partner's shoulder. "Calm down, it looked like

104

something pulled her under," he said.

"You're right. Maybe she'll get eaten by a shark." The man laughed.

The two men walked away, back to the docks.

When she opened her stinging eyes, Hanh found herself on an empty beach, coughing up water.

"Are you ok?" a familiar voice asked.

Hanh recovered her vision and, in the moonlight, saw Chau.

"I saw you being chased by those murderers. As soon as you jumped, I grabbed you before it was too late," Chau said.

Hanh didn't respond. She felt bile rising in her throat again and this time, she vomited, her body heaving. Between shaky breaths, she found her voice.

"The mermaid, they—"

"I know." Chau looked down as a tear dropped onto the sand. "She was my sister." She sobbed.

Hanh's vision blurred. "I'm so sorry."

Chau wiped her eyes. "There was nothing you could have done."

Chau breathed in. "My sister was out with her boyfriend tonight, but those men caught her in a net and sped away in their boat before he could stop them. Just as I was about to leave to go see you again, he swam in and told my family everything and that he needed my help to get my sister home."

Silence fell upon them before Hanh spoke.

"I'll make sure those guys pay for what they've done." Hanh placed a hand on Chau's shoulder.

"If you're planning to do this, maybe you could ask your friends to help?" Chau said. "Someone you trust?"

"With something like this?" Hanh shook her head. "I've had friends who left me over small disagreements we've had, so I don't … I really don't know about that. If anything, I'd rather do this alone than risk people screwing it up."

Chau paused, then nodded. "Just be careful, okay?"

With that, she helped Hanh get back to the beach near the pier, where she snuck back to her car and, soaking wet, drove back home.

Over the week, she focused everything on creating a plan to try to stop the men and the senseless murders.

But by the end of the week, Hanh's efforts paid off: she stumbled upon an online marine shop. When she opened it, she was shocked by what she saw. There, on the site, was a picture of the two men, displaying an enormous fish tail, but its shimmering colors weren't those of any normal fish. Concentrating on her research, she didn't hear her friend behind her.

"Hanh?" Leah said.

"Gah!" Hanh shut her laptop.

"Sorry, didn't mean to scare you." Leah sat down. "How are you feeling, by the way?"

She looked away. What was she supposed to say for something like this?

"If you're still upset from your near-drowning experience, you need to let me know so I can help, ok?" Leah said.

Hanh played along, "Thanks. Just give me some time. I'll be fine. Eventually."

Leah frowned, but decided to let her be. Maybe some happier news would cheer her up. "Guess what? Simon, your best friend from high school called. He said he'll be staying in town for two weeks. To save money, he's coming in late at night, so we'll need to go pick him up around midnight."

Hanh was ecstatic to hear that he'd be in town and she let it show. She hadn't seen him since they had graduated, but now was not the time to celebrate.

There were lives at stake.

"I'm going to go pick up some snacks," Hanh said. "I'll be back before we need to pick him up."

Instead of going to the store, she went back to the shack, this time with a plan. She remembered seeing fishing nets nearby. As she dug around the mess near the shack for them, she also found a ladder on its side. Perfect. She quietly set it up and would use it to climb onto the roof.

However, she didn't realize how heavy the nets were and she struggled to even put her foot on the first step. A few times she fell back down because of the weight of the net. She was out of breath but

106

remembered her promise to Chau. Lifting the net onto her back, she gave it one last effort. Slowly and carefully, she lifted it up inch by inch until she made it to the top of the shack with the huge net. The roof creaked under the weight. Still, she was determined to make it work. She pushed it to the edge of the roof and waited.

It wasn't long before they arrived. She heard the men and the sound of their catch flopping on the ground. When the men went to unlock the doors to the shack, Hanh shoved the heavy net over them.

They shouted and tangled themselves up in the net, unable to get it off.

Hanh leapt down and grabbed the netted mermaid by the tail and dragged her towards the sea. But the mermaid was so heavy that it was getting harder to keep going.

Hanh could hear the men cursing and arguing.

The mermaid looked up at Hanh as she struggled to get them to the water. "We're not going to get there in time—just save yourself."

"I'm not lea—"

The mermaid tugged the net away.

Hanh had no choice. She had failed. She had to leave the mermaid behind. She ran to the edge of the dock. She jumped in and swam as fast as she could. As she swam, she saw an anchored boat in the distance. She carefully swam around and hid behind it. She waited and watched as the men, who had managed to escape, tried to find her.

After some time, they eventually gave up and went back to drag their catch of the day back. As Hanh watched from behind the boat, she heard something swim up behind her. Panicked, she looked around.

To her relief, it was Chau. Together they waited in horror as the men cut the tail and hair off their catch before dumping the remains into the sea.

And all that they could do was watch.

Chau took Hanh to the shore not far from where she had parked.

"Just as I said, you can't stop this alone," Chau said.

"I know, but who knows what will happen to you mermaids if anyone knows you exist. My friends don't want to hurt you, but they might end up putting you in danger."

"But—"

"No, I want to be sure you're all safe. I'll stop this, alright?"

Before Chau could reply, they heard a strange sound.

"What's that?" Chau asked.

Hanh realized it was her cellphone, still intact thanks to its waterproof case. She opened it and saw Leah had been texting her: "Where are you? Did you forget we're supposed to pick up Simon at the airport tonight? I'm driving him home right now, meet you at home."

Hanh wanted to go after the murderers, but knew Leah would worry if she didn't return home. "I have to go home now; my friends are waiting for me."

Back at her car, Hanh realized that although she had forgotten about her friend coming, she had remembered to pack dry clothes, and she changed into them before driving off. That way, Leah wouldn't suspect anything; the last thing she needed was her friend poking around where she shouldn't.

When she entered the house, she nearly burst with joy when she saw the familiar face sitting next to Leah.

"Simon." Hanh said as she and her best friend hugged each other after so long. "How's it been?"

Leah smiled and left for bed to let them have their moment.

"Everything's good," Simon said. "I'm just hoping to meet up with my favorite people in the world before I start school again. What about you? Leah told me you've been having a hard time since almost drowning."

Hanh had forgotten about her near-drowning experience.

Simon put his hand on Hanh's shoulder. "You know if you ever want to talk about it, I'm always here for you. Just like in high school."

She thought back to her situation. While she still didn't want anyone else to know about the mermaids, the recent failure taught her she couldn't stop the men by herself.

"Well, actually, I do want to talk about something," Hanh said. "I need help."

"Anything," Simon said.

Hanh was hesitant to bring up her discovery, but figured he was the only help she could trust. She took a deep breath.

"After I got back to shore, I caught sight of some men carrying something. At first, I thought they were just fishermen bringing in a big fish, but when I got a better view of their catch, I was shocked. They had caught an endangered animal and chopped its tail off. Then they dumped its remains into the sea."

"Why didn't you tell anyone? The police, or even Leah?"

"They can't help."

"Why not?"

"Leah will probably just get the police involved, and they'll mess this up, which is why I'm asking you."

"What kind of animal did you see them catch?"

"I can't tell you right now, but I need help stopping them."

Simon still had a perplexed expression, but nodded.

The next night, Hanh told Leah she would be out shopping with Simon. Leah didn't seem to think much of it.

When they arrived, the men were not back yet.

It wasn't long before they heard a truck pull up. She gestured to Simon to hide with her behind a nearby boat.

The two of them peeked up and saw the two men carrying their catch of the night.

"That's them," Hanh whispered.

The men headed inside the shack with a helpless creature squirming in a net.

"Let's get closer," Hanh said.

She and Simon crept closer and peered into a window.

Overhead clouds cleared away from the moon exposing the bright evening light. Hanh and Simon's shadow showed up on the floor inside the shack.

The men saw the shadows too and turned around to face the trespassers.

One of them pulled out a gun.

"Run!" Hanh yelled. She and Simon sprinted towards the water. Behind them they heard a gunshot.

They jumped into the frigid water.

Something grabbed Hanh's hand and pulled her quickly through the water. Simon was hanging on to her other arm.

It was Chau. Chau took hold of both of them. "Hold your breath," she said.

She dove underwater with both of them. They resurfaced along a different shoreline.

"Looks like you took my advice this time." Chau pointed to Simon.

"Yeah, and it didn't work," Hanh said.

Before Chau could reply, Simon spoke up. "You have a tail."

Hanh was about to explain before Simon interrupted. "You're a mermaid, aren't you? I haven't seen one since I was five."

They gasped at Simon's response.

"You've met one before?" Hanh said. "When?"

"I made friends with a mermaid around my age back in Vietnam. When their mother got caught, I helped her and her family escape … that was the last time I saw them."

"What was her name?" Chau asked.

"Chau," he said. "I hope she's safe, wherever she is."

Chau and Hanh gasped.

"You're Simon?" Chau said.

He stared at the mermaid for a moment. "It can't be. Chau, is that you?"

Chau smiled before she leaned over to hug him. They wanted to catch up on what had happened before Hanh interrupted. "How come you never told me you knew about mermaids?"

"You never asked," Simon said.

"Good point," Hanh said.

Simon looked back. "But … those men we saw," Simon said. "What were they doing?"

"Killing for profit."

Simon's eyes widened. "What the hell are they thinking?"

"Profit blinds them," Hanh said.

"We've got to stop them," he said.

"But we need more help," Chau said. "Look, I get that you don't trust many people, Hanh, but neither did I until I met the both of you."

"Obviously we can't do this on our own," Simon said. "If we get our

110

friend Leah to help, it's still not enough. Chau, how many mermaids can you get to help?"

"Oh, you'll see." Chau smirked.

"Meet back at the docks tomorrow night," Hanh said.

The next day, Simon and Hanh were eating breakfast when Leah came into the dining room and sat at the table.

"So, do you guys have anything planned for the day?" Leah asked.

Simon and Hanh shared a look.

"Leah, there's something I got to tell you," Hanh said.

Together, Hanh and Simon explained everything.

"Really, guys?" Leah said. "You expect me to believe that?"

"No," Hanh said, "but we'll prove it. Come on, we have a friend we'd like you to meet."

***

The sun had just set and Leah had gotten over the shock of meeting a real mermaid.

"Okay, here's the plan," Hanh said, "all we need to do is get the men into the water."

"Yes." Chau smirked. "We'll take care of the rest."

Not long after, when darkness had fallen, the men returned to their shack with yet another helpless catch. As they dragged the netted mermaid from the back of their truck, there was a loud splash. And then another. And another.

They both looked around and caught sight of a mermaid tail flipping into the water.

"Looks like it's our lucky night," the first man said. "Grab the net."

The mermaid continued to jump freely splashing him with each flip of her tail.

He pulled out a gun.

The other man dragged a heavy net over to the water. He crouched down with the net ready.

Before the men could do anything, Hanh, Simon, and Leah charged at them without warning, shoving them into the water.

Unfortunately, the man with the gun grabbed Hanh's ankle and dragged her down into the water with him. The others screamed for her.

Hanh gasped for air before being pushed under water.

And then it was silent. Simon and Leah couldn't see her anywhere. In the darkness, they couldn't see what was happening under the water. The splashing had stopped.

"Where is she?" Leah screamed.

Simon points to the far end of the dock. "Over there. Come on."

The two of them sprinted towards the figure in the water splashing.

When they got there, Hanh was in the water gripping the edge of the dock, panting for air.

Simon and Leah crouched down and reached out to grab her arms. Before they could pull her closer, she became light in their grasp and seemed to fly up out of the water.

Simon and Leah jumped back from the force. There was Chau hoisting Hanh out of the water and placing her on the ground.

"Are you okay?" Leah asked.

Hanh didn't respond for a moment. Instead, she coughed up some water. Then she turned to them and smiled. "I am, but what about the men?"

Chau chuckled. "Don't worry. We took good care of them. I'll tell you all about it." She pointed towards the shack. "But first, can you get my friend?"

Simon and Leah ran back.

Chau leaned closer to Hanh. "Maybe as the world changes, you can tell people about us and save more of us in the future just like what you and your friends did. I know trusting others is difficult but, you always have us watching your back."

Hanh began to tear up as she hugged Chau.

EQUINOX
by Madison Zinnekah

Like the morning dew,
Birds migrate and go slowly,
As do spring and fall

CRYONICS
by Madison Zinnekah

Ice is quite chilling
Hope for new life is thrilling
And thus fulfilling

AUTUMN'S PLAYGROUND
by Madison Zinnekah

Leaves fall to the ground
Like children run to a park
In a rushed flurry

SEA

by Brian Nguyen

Origin of life
Home to some, ruthless to all
Cradle of mankind

DIRT

by Brian Nguyen

Full of life and death
New beginnings, bitter ends
Mourned and loved by all

ROSE

by Brian Nguyen

Elegant, painful
Love for some, loss for others
Pricks the ignorant

WATER
by Brian Nguyen

Swift and elegant
Plentiful, strong, and gentle
Provider of life

SCHOOL
by Brian Nguyen

Tedious, stressful
Satisfaction is so rare
Few can enjoy it

FIRE
by Brian Nguyen

Bright and powerful
Best when wielded properly
Used for good and bad

MISFORTUNE

by Khanh Tran

"Scarecrow"
Birds feast on my crops
I try to scare them away
They still never leave

"Flood"
Water keeps rising
Rises now above my knees
I can't find my son

"Blaze"
The scorching wildfire
Spreads like a plague and blazes
Across the county

My Friend

by Thomas Tran

March 30

Mom got me this journal to help keep track of things, because apparently, I can't be trusted to stay after school until 5 and get all my homework done. Oh well, it shouldn't be that hard to work on club affairs, class assignments and this at the same time, right?

September 4

I lied; I need the journal after all. I'm staying up to 11 working on *Physics* alone. I don't even have any other homework to do, it's literally all just Physics! I feel my regret growing

November 1

Grandpa's … not okay. I don't like how fast this is escalating either. It's already been 2 weeks since Mom visited him and found him with full-body psoriasis *overnight* and his body's rapidly failing. This journal isn't for me anymore, I've been using it to help track treatments and appointments. I know it's inevitable but God please just give us the end of the month at least

November 15

Grandpa doesn't recognize any of us anymore. We're talking to him, helping him remember us, but I had to step out. I keep hearing something ticking. Grandpa doesn't have any clocks. I don't know what's going on

November 26

It's over. Grandpa's dead.
The ticking got louder over the crying. I heard something being cut too, a string or something. Might just be nerves. I don't think any of us will be okay for a while

117

November 28

We buried Grandpa today. I spoke at his funeral. The ticking went away afterwards. I might've just been drained that day I don't know

February 3

The ticking came back. I was walking to school when I heard the ticking again. It got louder and then there was a car crash, fire and everything. I heard the cut string again while firefighters and police showed up but the guy was definitely dead. It stopped afterwards … is this a pattern? Need to track this

March 11

I heard it again, walking past a girl at my high school. Not as loud as the other times, but I still heard the ticks. She didn't look okay. Class was about to start so I couldn't stop. I wonder what happened

March 13

I heard the cutting sound while finishing up math homework. I started to see something; I hope I'm wrong

March 16

I wasn't wrong. We had a memorial for her during lunch; her name was Alex. I couldn't sit still during it. I started hearing more ticking too; I think it's from the people around me. Some are louder, some are softer, but they're all there

Every time I hear the ticking, I hear the cutting sound and then someone dies. Are they all going to die too?

March 28

Needed to test the theory, I picked out a guy; Mickael was his name. His ticking kept changing–sharp, low, slow, fast, soft–but it was always louder than other people so he was ideal. He was in my PE class, but never had to do anything because he really needs his inhaler or he'd die. Don't know why they let a really weak kid into high school PE, but not my problem.

Ended up stealing his inhaler and shoving him in a back room and waiting for his ticking to speed up and the cutting sound. I checked him after it too; he had no pulse

… I just killed someone to test a theory. Why don't I feel anything?

April 5
The school found Mickael last week and suspect murder. The cops are running an investigation. Had to keep my head down. Thank God we have these face masks, made lying *so* much easier when they interviewed me and my PE class. I think they're focusing on some other kid, Billy

April 13
The investigations are still going. The cops are starting to ignore Billy. They might find out it was me

April 18
I'm starting to hear whispers. Something's following me. I don't know what it is, but it always stays out of the corner of my eye. I tried cornering it, but there were just shadows. Might just be me working too hard. Can't wait for the weekend

April 20
The shadows look clearer now. I see a masked man walking in the crowd. No one else can see it. I think it knows. Every time I see it, the ticking comes back. I feel cold

May 10
It can talk to me. Said that the cops would call it off and the school was going to pretend things never happened. It keeps staying with me

May 24
I couldn't focus in class again. The ticking got louder. I hear explosions and gunfire with it, and more cutting too. I don't see the Masked Man that much anymore. It said it was busy

June 3

Been more murders on the news recently. Dad's getting nervous. He keeps telling us to be careful. The Masked Man said I shouldn't be worried, though. It says it'll make sure our work isn't discovered

… I won't let Dad find out it was me. I'll do it tonight

June

Too loud, everything's *too loud!* Everyone leaves me alone, but the ticking won't stop!
Need to do something to shut everything up! The Masked Man says it knows something that'll work but

```
 g        o     D      W       h  Y      I   s
  E   v    E   r   y        T   h   I   N    g
     s       O    l       O       U    D
```

Fourteen years later…

I looked towards the desk where my journal laid. The bedroom was dark. There was a stillness, as if even the shadows that danced in the night had gone to sleep.

Tick. Tock.

I turned in my bed with a sleepy grumble. The ticking's not there. It's not, I just imagined it. It's been years since I started to hear it, and it never bothered my sleep. It just bothered me every waking moment! I had spent years killing for a moment of peace, so why now–

Tick. Tock.

Nope, nope, nope, nope! It's not there, it's not there! I'm just ima—

Tick. Tock.

Tick. Tock.

I pulled a pillow over my head. "Can you not?" I asked. There was a silent pause. *Did it actually?* I dared to hope before it started again, louder and stronger. I gritted my teeth and struggled to cover my ears. The sound echoed in my head, each tick louder and faster than the last.

Ticktockticktockticktockticktockticktockticktockticktockticktockticktockticktockt

icktock

"Shut up," I growled. I slammed my fists against the bed and pushed myself up. My eyes snapped open with a roar in my throat. "Get out of my head–!"

I stopped. This wasn't my room.

I was standing now, somehow. My room was gone, replaced with a vast void that stretched as far as I could see. Silver strings flowed through the empty space, slow and listless.

Tick.

A chill ran down my spine as my body processed the cold. I rubbed my forearms and looked around. This *emptiness* felt wrong.

Tock.

My brow twitched at the still present ticking. If I could still hear it, then there had to be someone else here. I whirled around and tried to find the source before my face paled. I shouldn't have looked.

"Finally. You've come, friend."

It was the Masked Man. It was as tall as always in its plain black suit, its face still concealed by a white face mask that had small, downward crescents for eyelids and a thin smile that reached from ear to ear.

My eyes burned. My head pounded as I felt something crack with every growing second. I swallowed my bile as I hurried to look away.

Tick tock tick tock tick tock tick tock tick tock—

What was that? *What was that?*

From behind, some creature's black, skeletal frame loomed over the Masked Man, a rumble coming from its ichor-dripping maw. I couldn't resist a shiver as I noticed the small details. For something supposedly alive, it felt so cold, so hollow, so *wrong*. The Masked Man waved its hand and the thing vanished, but that fearful sense still remained.

"Excuse my 'excitement' there, friend, I couldn't resist myself." The Masked Man's head tilted to the side with mild mischief. "After all, you've been of great use to me these past fourteen years."

My dread rose. "What are you talking about?"

Tick tock tick tock tick tock tick tock tick tock tick tock …

"Well, you've been making my job much easier, haven't you, friend?" The Masked Man shrugged, as if pointing out the obvious. "Managing and ending lifelines can be such a hassle, but you did half the work for me. And all it took was for us to hear the same thing."

The Masked Man reached for a particular string. I paled as I felt my heart stop when a sharp nail hooked onto it. "You harvested so many souls for me," the Masked Man noted as it coiled the string around its finger. I felt my strength leave me as I collapsed, before something caught me. The same string partially coiled around the Masked Man's finger was caught against my neck and stopped me from falling any further.

"What are you doing?" I tried asking again between weak gasps. The Masked Man tilted its head back and chuckled, its voice suddenly distorted now.

"You were of use to me. You've killed many these fourteen years, but I'm done playing with you. You can leave now." Its finger tightened against the string, slowly cutting it through.

Tock tick tick tock tick tock tick tock tick tock tick tock tick tock—

Snip.

LATEST SCOOPS
by Stella Nguyen

Latest Scoop with William and Hexa (and Milo)

CHARACTERS
Hexa, sportscaster (unhelpful friend)
William, sportscaster (unhelpful friend)
Milo, pitiful friend (scapegoat)
Werewolf

FADE IN

EXT. WOODS - NIGHT
A dark clearing in the middle of the woods. The full moon rises high above the scene.

Scene fades in on MILO running out of the trees with WILLIAM following close behind. He is holding a microphone. CAMERA cuts to a large werewolf chasing them, close on their tail. It cuts back to William, who looks very excited and frazzled.

WILLIAM
Good evening, folks, today is an active day for us, isn't it Hexa?

HEXA (O.S.)
That's right William!

Camera cuts to HEXA, jogging beside William. The werewolf disregards them and instead sprints after Milo. They pay no attention to their screaming friend.

WILLIAM

We're reporting live from The Woods of Freya, where a werewolf was spotted just today! Not common around these parts, are they? Maybe it was lured in by the sweet scent of curiosity or Milo's quivering fear!

CAMERA switches to Milo climbing a tree as the werewolf circles him.

MILO

(screams)

I am literally about to die and you're cracking jokes?

CAMERA back to William and Hexa who are a safe distance from the tree.

WILLIAM

Werewolves started appearing two years after the original rift was opened. Their claws and speed were quite the surprise for our "battle-hardened" warriors.

HEXA

Say William, mind explaining what the rift is for the new viewers?

WILLIAM

(laughs)

Hexa, I doubt we have any new viewers this far into the apocalypse, but anything for you. Remember the days when everything was simple? People even chose to be ignorant of the astral plane. Good times.

HEXA

Of course, thank Athena we managed to survive as long as we did. Don't know how we managed to avoid all those Gorgons. They were no match for my trusty sword though.

MILO (O.S.)
How about helping me with a bit of that, then?

WILLIAM
Yes, thank Artemis they took pity on you, Hexa, you poor child!

Hexa throws a nasty glare at William.

HEXA
Ahem, the rift?

WILLIAM
Of course. But what much else is there to say? There's a fine line between the physical realm and the astral realm. Teenagers playing with a Ouija board or summoning demons without the proper steps shakes that line and can leave a little opening for those cretins, but imagine the catastrophe that would come if it were done on a greater scale.

HEXA
Yikes.

WILLIAM
Of course, there were the skeptics who refused to even acknowledge the ideas of a spiritual realm. But there were a few who managed to start the project just to prove them wrong—you know, because being right is a lot more important than keeping the world normal and safe and all that jazz. We're looking at you, Mr. Aiden of the SCC.

HEXA
Yeah, thanks a lot, Aiden.

WILLIAM

Well from here folks, you should know what happened next. They got too close, breached that fine line, yada yada, mass chaos ensued. Honestly, if you don't know what's been going on, where have you been?

HEXA

Now William, let's not disregard the ones who only recently got cured from being a statue or had been living under a rock 'til now.

WILLIAM

You make a good point; you make a good point. But anyway, we've ranted enough about the past—let's talk about the now, like these exciting, new creatures!

HEXA

(sighs)
There goes the free recap. But sure, we don't have all night, so let's get the show on the road. Today, we're discussing the dangers of werewolves, yeah?

WILLIAM

Yeah, like the one Milo's distracting.

William points to Milo. CAMERA cuts to Milo, ACTION MUSIC plays. Milo swings a spear at the werewolf and yells a war cry. CAMERA cuts back to Hexa and William, and action music abruptly fades to DOCUMENTARY MUSIC.

WILLIAM

As we can see, Milo is defending himself from the big bad werewolf. See how he's avoiding its claws and teeth? Maybe the werewolves in your neighborhood aren't as dangerous or unstable as the ones in this area, but this one's got poison-coated claws. Not sure why, but maybe it's a foreign breed. Scandinavia, maybe?

HEXA

Maybe. Although most people don't last this long in a fight with a normal breed of these bad boys.

Hexa and William walk over to the werewolf, the CAMERA follows them as they slap the werewolf's behind. The werewolf yelps and turns its attention to Hexa, about to attack them, but Milo tackles it away. Hexa stands unfazed and continues to face the camera.

HEXA

But then again, most people aren't Milo.

Quick cut to Milo trying to stab the werewolf with his spear.

MILO

Can you two quit playing around and HELP ME?

WILLIAM

You may be wondering why instead of trying to rehabilitate this werewolf, as most are usually confined in their homes every full moon, we're attacking it. But, judging by its size, this isn't your ordinary werewolf. It's a pure werewolf.

HEXA

Gee William, what's a pure werewolf?

WILLIAM

Well, infected werewolves don't come out of nowhere! So, if you find yourself in front of one of these guys, you might as well just stab them before they eat you, because they're going to tear off your face. And trust me, that's not a pretty sight.

A DING comes from Hexa's PHONE and the camera focuses on Hexa.

HEXA

Looks like we got a question from one of our viewers! Eryach568 asks, "So, what about Milo? Aren't you worried he might die?"

WILLIAM

Ah, you must be new to our show. You see, it's because Milo worries so much for us he absolutely refuses for us to even get near his fights. Right Milo?

Quick cut to a blood-soaked Milo, on the verge of passing out. Milo flips the bird at the camera.

FADE OUT

END

180

by Andy Nguyen

Around us, the world flourishes.
Birds sing sweet nothings in our ears as the day begins.
Children laugh as they scribble with their pencils and crayons.
Doesn't this sound like the start to a perfect day?
Early in the morning, the sun begins to rise.
Faced with another day, people awaken,
Getting out of their warm beds,
Heading to work, venturing into the colorful world.
In their eyes, it's just another normal day
Jammed in the same train, unaware of their surroundings.
Kids flip through their textbooks.
Lost, they continue to strive for the future.
Months pass by, the same pattern repeats.
Nobody knows that life is about to make a one-eighty.
Overseas, something changes.
People are drafted and run out to war.
Quarters turn into pennies.
Red splatters on the streets.
Seconds pass like hours as they slink into obscurity.
The universe seems to be collapsing, not by God's hand, but by man's.
Unable to realize the damage, people slaughter each other.
Vultures pick at dead bodies of the fallen.
Waves of reinforcements march in, not wanting the war to continue.
X-ray satellites struggle to comprehend the atrocities inflicted on human
bodies.
Years pass by with no sight of an ending.
Zero make it out alive.

BROKEN COMPUTER

by Makea Linh Adams

Three years
I have tried.
Three years.
Something is wrong.
I cannot be fixed.
I have tried to reboot
A series of times.
Nothing works.

Nothing can be done.
Unsure of it all.
What is wrong?
Why won't I work?

Three years
I've been broken
I am just junk
Sitting in an old room
Waiting to be thrown out.

SORRY COMPUTER

by Sydney Dao

Shut down, sleep, restart
Oh, I can't bear this!
I can't bear to be apart

I'm sorry computer,
I know we've been together since day one
But my technological story
Has just begun

I'm sorry computer,
But I'm moving on
Away from the comfort of your blue sky
And rolling green lawn

I'm sorry computer,
But I've found someone new
Someone who doesn't lag, buffer, or glitch
Someone who can print assignments
When my friends are in a pinch

I'm sorry computer,
But this is for the best
It's time I hit that fateful button
And it's time for you to rest.

THE SUBJECT

by Brandon Nguyen

"TEST 122. NAME: MARTIN. Age: 24. Status: Volunteer," the computer stated.

The year was 2054. Another test for light-speed velocity began. The shuttle started preparing for its next glorious flight. Designed to stop exactly one microsecond after launch, it flashed off. Octavius, head scientist of the project, took his team to the crash site. One microsecond of light speed should be .186 miles. The team hurried, arriving there in minutes. They opened up the shuttle to find the subject, Martin. His hair had fallen off, his body was pressed into his chair, his organs were rearranged towards his back, the state of his face was unrecognizable.

A chilling sight the team had grown used to. Matthew, the lead assistant, opened the logs of the shuttle that monitored the patient. Skimming through them, he noticed they had achieved a major breakthrough. The subject had survived the acceleration to light speed and only died during deceleration. Most subjects died in the process of speeding up the shuttle to the speed of light, but Subject 122 *lived*.

Taking this as a sign they were on the right track, the team celebrated. Soon, they could have a working shuttle that could preserve humans through lightspeed travel. The team of scientists took the logs and headed back to their lab.

Octavius stayed behind at the scene. He peered at the body now sagging in the chair. People came to collect the body and he watched them take it away. Like his team, they paid no mind to the rearranged organs or indistinguishable face. To them, it was like throwing out trash. To think that this became the norm.

Octavius walked back to the lab where the rest of the team was. They had already opened up the camera and slowed it to a billionth of a second. He saw their eager eyes as they examined the subject. While 122 did survive the acceleration process, it was clear that he wasn't in a living state. His body was completely ruined, but he was still alive for a moment. With more precautionary measures, the project could eventually let the subjects live.

While the other scientists cheered, Octavius thought about its implications. Subject 122 would go down in history. But that's how he would be remembered: Subject 122. A number. Octavius thought of the young Martin, only twenty-four when he volunteered for such a project.

They weren't running out of test subjects anytime soon. They had a near-infinite number of volunteers at their disposal, and if those people turned away, they could always use inmates.

Octavius examined Subject 122. The subject didn't even know he died. In less than a second, the subject's bodily functions ceased to continue. He doubted any mind could comprehend a fate like this.

He thought back to when they first announced the light speed project, about how much funding they had received, and all the people who wanted to help. Light speed travel would revolutionize mankind's ability to explore as well as travel. It would change how resources and goods were transported. It would be a revolution greater than anything the world has ever seen. He remembered his excitement as the world supported his findings. It still did. Each test taught them a new valuable lesson.

Octavius thought back to Subject 1. He didn't remember the name of Subject 1 or their face. It was just Subject 1.

In his moment of thought, he was pulled over. Laura, his wife and a fellow scientist, squeezed a hand on his shoulder. The team was excited about their findings, but Octavius didn't join them. "Are you okay?" she asked.

"I'm fine," he said.

"Then why don't you celebrate with us?"

"I'll come later."

Knowing her husband, she went and left him alone. Octavius pretended to enjoy himself until he got home where he opened his computer.

Initiating the lab program, he began to open up records of former tests. He scrolled through the list: Subject 1, Subject 2, Subject 3, Subject 4.

The list went on. He should be documenting their latest results with 122. Instead, he opened Subject 1's file.

Joseph Randolph, 31. Joseph Randolph was the name of Subject 1. Peering through the other files, he found names he had long forgotten. Pierre, Otto, Willow, Paris, Keiren. Their names were now designated by the word "Subject" and a number. Each of them left a distorted and mangled corpse thanks to this project.

He hesitated. This wasn't what he wanted when he founded the project. Earning his degrees and awards, becoming a great scientist as famous as Einstein and Newton. Where did it go wrong? His work was groundbreaking but he didn't feel like it. His excitement was long gone.

The door opened and his wife entered. She caught him as he scrolled through the list of subjects. "What are you doing?"

"Finishing up some work." He paused. "Do you remember the name of Subject 1?" Octavius asked.

"Should I? It's been three years, I believe."

"I guess not." He continued scrolling through the subjects, not turning to face her.

"Get some sleep. We have important work to do tomorrow," she said.

He didn't answer.

"Don't worry about this," she said with desperation.

"How much longer until we're done?" he asked.

"Pardon?"

"How much longer before we finish our work?" he said.

"I don't know, maybe four or five years."

"How many people will die in that time?"

"Listen, I understand how you feel, but we have to keep working. If we stop now, the people that have died will die in vain."

"And we'll just work harder for each person we kill," he said.

"We don't kill anyone. They volunteered for this. One hundred and twenty-two people have died already. We need to finish our work in memory of them."

And at that moment, Octavius's mind wandered off. Was it impossible to be both moral and a great man? "Then why should we send off another person to die?" He thought aloud. "We've already ended so

134

many. What if it takes a hundred more tests? Two hundred? Three hundred? Isn't it a contradiction to kill more in memory of them? How many people are going to die for an experiment?" He motioned to the long list of Subjects, the pictures next to their names showing not their living faces, but unrecognizable faces mutilated by light speed.

"Does the glorious end justify these means? We've killed so many that we can't remember any of their names. All they are to us are subjects. They aren't people. We've been treating them as subjects to throw away. We've thrown away one hundred and twenty-two lives, and all we have to show for it is that we think we're almost there. I didn't start this project to be a murderer."

He looked down, the guilt of every subject's lost life crashing down on him. "We celebrated the death of a man today. Doesn't that bother you? Today, we celebrated a man dying for results. We had a party and cheered. We enjoyed ourselves while their lives are over. He was twenty-four. He had the rest of his life ahead of him but he decided this would be for some greater good—"

"And that was his choice," she interrupted him.

Octavius sighed. "Maybe you're right. Maybe I'm just rambling. I'll come up in a bit."

He sat there in thought as Laura left. He turned off his computer, as his thoughts came to a conclusion and his resolve hardened. He woke up the next morning and headed towards the lab. He called media outlets and prepared for a major conference meeting to show their results to the world. Light speed travel was an inevitability, the only thing they didn't know was when it would come. He remembered his first presentation, discussing the uses of light-speed travel. Near instantaneous transport as far as a human could imagine. Now, he would announce the biggest change anyone could ever expect.

His wife and the rest of his team stood alongside him on the stage. Taking out his papers, he prepared his speech. Clearing his throat, he greeted the media and the rest of the audience, from major tech companies and their sponsors to various world leaders. This was the work the world had been waiting for.

He took a deep breath in as he reached the climax of the speech.

"When I first started this project three years ago, I had great hopes. Hopes of this technology improving our way of life hundreds of times over. But now, while I see the prospects of our work, and all the potential and good it will do, I can no longer see it as the morally correct decision. The lives it had cost can never justify the outcome. At this moment, I announce the end of the project and resign from my place as head researcher. I refuse to continue working for an outcome that requires the prices of hundreds to be achieved."

Silence followed. He left the stage alone, followed by the stares of countless eyes.

And while a hundred and twenty-two souls weighed on him, while he was shunned by the world, while his friends look at him in disgust, while the families of the deceased spat on him, while his wife called him a fool, while his family forgot him, while his life collapsed and while his wealth disappeared, while his name faded into nothingness, he was fine because he knew in his heart that he had done the right thing.

Without him, the project would never sacrifice anyone ever again.

MATH

by Alham Attaee

Math
stressful, depressing
tiring, learning, talking
variables, sleep, equations, fatigue
less sleeping, time flying, slow pacing
sleepy, boring
Work

FARM

by Mike Nguyen

The farmer had a pen with lots of charm
There were chickens who lay down in the barn
And sheep who loved chewing twigs
The farmer fed cows and pigs
And the horse loved to mess around on the farm

FLOWERS

by Mike Nguyen

New seeds are planted
And the flowers grow and shine
As Spring passes by

RUNNING

by Vincent Quach

Cross Country
Fast, Trail, Long-Distance, Open Air
Running, Jogging, Pacing, Following, Tracking, Tailing
Muscle Cramps, Leg Pains, Sweat, Gritted Teeth, Rapid Heart Rate
Throwing, Jumping, Sprinting, Hurdling, Flipping
Speedy, Precise, Race Track
Track and Field

READY TO RACE

by Vincent Quach

A start to the day at the line,
And we're off without a whine.
Every mile covered
The more we suffered,
Nevertheless, we finish at the line.

A HOT RUN

by Vincent Quach

Out in the baking sun,
We're out for a scorching run.
Dry and dusty all over,
And we're sweating with odor.
In the end, we won, not the sun.

DRAGON, HERO, AND PRINCESS

by Hillary Nguyen

BARDS HAVE ALWAYS SUNG tales of a Dragon, Hero, and Princess. The Dragon leaves death in its wake. Only one sword, the Sword of Fate, can slay the Dragon and such a powerful sword chooses its wielder. The one who can pull the Sword out of its sheath is made the Chosen One, the Hero. The kingdom cheers after the Choosing and sends the Hero off. The Hero slays the Dragon and is awarded the Princess's hand in marriage, and they all live happily ever after.

Although decades have passed, the tradition still stands today.

But Princess Eliana refused to let fate bind her to someone she didn't choose. She gritted her teeth. Any day now, she would force that wretched Sword to acknowledge her. She would pull it out and kill the havoc-wreaking dragon and she would prove she was the rightful heir to the throne, not some random Hero. Her hands gripped the handle of a sword, far inferior to that Sword, and swung at her target. The training dummy fell to the ground in clean halves.

Eliana turned to the servant waiting a distance behind her. "Well, what is it?"

"It's about the Sword of Fate, Your Highness."

"What? Did another fool get burnt trying to steal it?"

The servant coughed. "No, the Sword has chosen someone."

She narrowed her eyes. "Who?"

"Someone from the batch of commoners that Baron Calia sent over." The servant stared down. "The officiating ceremony will occur tonight. The King has sent the commoner to rest for now."

Eliana's hand trembled and she fought the urge to throw her sword down. She inhaled and the servant flinched. "Put the sword back in the rack." She handed it over. "I'll be going now."

***

140

When Eliana entered the throne room, all she saw was red. It burned her eyes and throat. She took her seat a step below the king. The king sat on his throne, giving the customary speech to bless the Hero.

She turned to the man on one knee in front of her father, the supposed Hero. The only word that came to mind was … unremarkable. He had a plain appearance and common features. Decent, but she had seen people far more pleasing to the eye. Nothing stood out about him except his trembling hands and puffy eyes, presumably from crying.

She glared at the pitiful sight. What about this person made the Sword choose him? What did he have that she didn't?

As was customary, the Hero unsheathed the sword and pledged to protect the kingdom. She watched him fumble to take it out and stutter on his words. It was clear that he had never held a sword before. She clenched her fists as he finished.

The ceremony came to an end and the king sent the Hero off to rest before he would leave tomorrow to slay the dragon.

As the nobles left and the servants cleared the area, she turned to the king. "Father, I'm going with the Hero."

The king peered down at Eliana with a distant gaze. "It doesn't matter either way. Make your preparations." He descended his throne, turned, and walked away, without a backwards glance.

***

In the morning, Eliana headed to the Hero's room. "Is he done preparing?" she asked the knight guarding the door.

He nodded and announced her arrival. "Hero, Her Highness is here."

A crash sounded in the room. "Uh, yes, come in," a frantic voice sounded.

Eliana walked in. The guest room designated for the Hero was lavish, befitting that of a noble. She stared at the Hero; his eyes unsure of where to look until they settled on the ground. He looked rather small in such a large room. She turned to the side. "If you're ready, then let's go. I already have my bag."

The Hero looked up at her, confused.

"The King has granted me permission to go with you. You needed a traveling companion anyways."

He stammered. "I don't mean to be rude, but what about your duties, Your Highness?"

"What could be more important than ensuring that the Hero doesn't die on his way to the Dragon?" Eliana heard him gulp. She stared at him from the corner of her eyes. There was a flicker of relief on his face. She frowned. As she thought, everyone was foolish, sending an inexperienced person into the Dragon's Lair.

They approached the royal stables. A stable boy led two freshly bathed and brushed black stallions, muscles glistening in the sun, saddled up and ready to go.

The Hero flinched.

"Have you never ridden a horse before?" Eliana struggled to suppress the irritation in her voice. *Seriously, why did the Sword choose this pansy?*

The Hero shook his head. "I never had to back home, and we came here in a wagon."

She turned to the stable boy. "Take *Master* back and bring me a more docile one. Bring me *Fair Maiden*."

The stable boy returned with a sluggish old mare who trotted cautiously forward. Eliana handed the reins to the Hero. "This one's yours."

"The docile one?"

"You're inexperienced. Do you really want to ride *Valiant?*" She motioned to the remaining black stallion—a horse far more suitable for their long journey. Valiant snorted and glared at the Hero.

The Hero stepped behind Eliana. "Good point."

The stable boy assisted them both up, Eliana first, who tightened the reins. Valiant shook his head in protest, but obeyed nonetheless.

Once on Fair Maiden, The Hero stared at the loose reins that were placed into his hands. "Do I have to ride while leaving?"

"Just hold the reins and pretend to look like you know what you're doing. Fair Maiden will follow us. We'll ride once we're out of the castle grounds." She guided Valiant along the cobbled streets. In between the clop, clop, clop of their hooves, she heard a sigh of relief behind her. As much as she disliked him, she had to honor his dignity.

As they left the castle, the sounds of people cheering and sending their regards followed them. It irritated her and she rode faster. The cheering died down when they were a distance off. She peered back at the Hero who was now a good distance behind. "Well, hurry up now."

He gulped. "Now?"

"There's no time to waste."

He had his arms around the horse's neck. "How?" The reins were dragging on the ground.

Once again, she wanted to whack the Sword for its decision. She pulled back the reins and dismounted. She tied her horse to a tree.

After a moment of attempting but failing to teach him how to properly hold onto the reins and steer, she massaged her forehead. "Get off. It's clear you can't control even the simplest of beasts, so we'll have to ride together." She waited as he hesitated.

Without a word, she helped him off the horse, or more accurately, caught him as he stumbled down.

They walked in silence to a nearby village, Easton, where she left Fair Maiden, dropping a few coins in a villager's hand.

She peered at the Hero. "It'll be dark soon and there won't be another village for a couple of miles. Can you handle camping out?" She looked at the bag of coins in her hand. "I accounted for any traveling expenses, including lodging if needed, but it's best to save for emergencies."

He made an awkward smile. "Yeah, that much I can handle."

"Good. We can travel a decent distance before the sun sets." She motioned to Valiant. "I'll get on first. You will ride bareback with a pad. Do you need someone else to help you up?" She took his silence as a yes and called a villager over. Eliana maneuvered her way up onto the saddle and waited as he was helped up behind her.

"Put your arms around me so you don't fall. Don't clamp your legs on its flanks." She kicked the stirrups. "And move with the horse. Don't be so stiff." She felt his arms tighten around her as the horse trotted.

They were far from Easton and entered a forest. The sun would set in another hour or two. Eliana wanted to travel farther but clouds gathered in the sky and there was a rumble. She frowned. A storm was approaching. "Let's find shelter now."

They walked deeper into the forest where they found a cave. Eliana grabbed twigs, a rock, and a piece of flint from her bag. She started a fire. They sat in silence for a bit before the Hero spoke. "Your Highness, I was wondering if—"

"No need for that title. Just call me Eliana. And I'll call you by your name in return." She paused. "I never asked for your name." She hadn't thought about it and it was never mentioned during the Ceremony. Everyone simply knew the Hero as the Hero.

"It's Brier, Your Hi—Eliana."

"Don't look so nervous. I'm the one who asked to be less formal. Besides, I'd prefer to not call you Hero." *Because he didn't deserve that title.* She glanced at the hilt poking out of his bag. "You don't have experience with swords, right? I'll hold on to it for now." She reached for it. When her hand touched the hilt, a spark ignited and burnt her finger tip. She drew back. Stupid sword.

Brier stared at the sword, a hint of confusion in his eyes. And *pity.*

She narrowed her eyes, a stinging pain in her throat. "*What?*"

He looked away. "I'm sorry."

She snapped. "Look me in the eye."

He froze, but did so.

A lightning strike flashed outside, lighting up her glare.

"Why was it you? You don't even know how to use a sword!" She tightened her fists. "I spent my entire life trying to claim the Sword, while you were just bumbling in the countryside."

"I'm sorry."

She scoffed. "Is that all you know how to say?" Silence filled the cave, only disrupted by the constant rumble of thunder. Eliana laid on the ground, her back facing him. She closed her eyes, ignoring the sound of his muffled breaths, drawn out as he tried not to cry.

***

Eliana woke up to the scent of cooked meat and the sound of a crackling fire. She peered across the cave at Brier. He startled at her gaze but offered a skewered piece of meat.

She grabbed it and blew to cool it before she took a bite.

She set the finished skewer down. "You know how to hunt?"

He brightened a bit at her words. "Yes, just small animals though. I caught

144

a rabbit while you were asleep and skinned it." There was a glimmer of hope in his eyes. "Was it alright?"

She murmured a vague response, but he looked relieved. Eliana inhaled. There was no point in getting angry now. The Sword had already made its decision. She examined Brier. "You don't know how to ride a horse or hold a sword, but you can hunt and cook. Where did you grow up?"

He made a nervous smile. "I was in an orphanage. I took care of the younger kids and helped with cooking, cleaning, all the house chores. Hunting and gathering whatever I could find. When I had free time, I worked on the garden in the backyard."

"Is that so?" She glanced down. None of that would help defeat a dragon. She calculated the journey's length. It would take about three days to reach the Dragon's lair, if they took breaks between walking and riding. They couldn't strain the horse too much. Three days. She could teach him sword techniques but it wouldn't be enough. He had to learn the basics and master it to slay the Dragon. Naturally, such a feat would be impossible in so short a time.

She stared at her own sword tucked into her belt and laid it down on the ground. So, what if the Sword of Fate was the only sword that could kill the Dragon? Surely, a normal sword could still harm it. She could strike its vital points, weakening it before directing Brier to make the final killing blow.

In the middle of her pondering, she felt his stare on her. "What is it?"

He straightened. "Nothing. It's just … I was thinking of the rumors."

She raised her eyebrows. "Oh? What rumors?"

He looked down.

"Like I said, there's no need to be formal. And it's not like I can execute you. You're in an important position and I don't care much for rumors anyways."

Brier gulped. "Everyone knew that you trained from a young age so I was so sure that even though I was chosen, you could still use the Sword."

She frowned, and he hid himself beneath a nervous smile. Before he could dig himself into a deeper pit, she stood up. "Get up. You need to train."

She went to a clearing outside the cave, Brier trailing behind. She

145

unsheathed her sword. "The most important thing is your stance. Watch me carefully." She placed one foot forward and balanced herself. She took a few swings, then a few more in slow motion. "Alright, you try."

He hesitantly pulled the Sword out and attempted to mimic her posture. She moved his arm a bit and nudged his feet further apart. She stepped a distance back. "Take a few swings now." He swung wildly like he was hacking at foliage.

She sighed. "Think of the Sword as an extension of yourself. Every move you make should be purposeful. Don't just swing wildly."

She made him swing continuously to get comfortable holding the Sword. It was a relief that he was better at learning swordsmanship than riding a horse.

Not wanting to impede their progress, they continued to travel, with a few breaks to rest and for Brier to keep practicing.

As the sun began to set, Brier motioned for her to stop the horse. He jumped off and ran towards some bushes. He kneeled and pushed a few leaves aside. Eliana hovered behind him. He opened up a hand to her, showing her blueberries. "We can eat these."

A slight smile appeared on her face. "Why so excited?"

His face flushed. "Ah, sorry. Good berries like these were hard to find near my village."

They camped for the night next to a stream of water in the forest. Eliana plopped a few berries in her mouth, savoring the sweet taste.

Brier stared at the sky as he chewed on a berry. "What made you want to take up the sword?"

She glanced at him. "It might be a long story."

"I don't mind."

"All right then." She set herself down on a log. "When I was younger, I learned about the tales of the Hero and Dragon. Every child does. But I couldn't stand it when I learned I had to marry the chosen Hero. That person would become the true ruler of the kingdom while I'd just be a queen who had to host tea parties."

She smirked. "I've never wanted to do what others wanted me to. I figured that if I trained and became strong enough, I could be the Hero and inherit the throne. I'd marry someone of my choosing who would respect me as an equal and let me rule."

"And the King and everyone else just let you train?"

"The nobles and the royal advisers were against it. I couldn't even talk with my father. He was too busy, as always. For days, I tried to get an audience so I could have a sword master to train me. Finally, though, my nanny helped me run away from the castle to a cabin in the forest where my father's sword master lived." She laughed at the memory. "I threatened to camp outside his house until he trained me like he did for my father."

"And so, he agreed?"

"Yes. I trained under him for the next few days. He was my mentor." She murmured the next words. "And a far better father than my actual one." She was silent for a minute. "Then a messenger sent from the king relayed his words: 'Stop this foolishness and come back.' I didn't really have much of a choice. I returned home but visited him every day to train until he was too old to hold a sword."

"You managed to get what you wanted though, didn't you?"

"I suppose so. Although I didn't get everything I wanted." She stared at the Sword next to Brier.

He coughed, guilt clear on his face. "So how was your nanny? Did she get in trouble for helping you escape?"

"Not really. I made sure no one could blame her."

Brier smiled. "It's nice to know that you have someone so loyal at your side."

Eliana glanced aside. "Not anymore."

His smile disappeared. "What happened?"

"She died protecting me from assassins. I was young and inexperienced back then, still learning the sword."

"I'm sorry."

"Why are you apologizing for something you didn't do?" She smiled. "Are you saying you had a hand in the assassination attempts?"

His face paled. "Of course not."

She chuckled. "I jest. I doubt you're capable of such a thing."

He sighed in relief. "Please don't joke about that kind of thing."

"I'll keep that in mind."

"We should sleep. We need enough energy for tomorrow."

***

There were two days left. Eliana opened her eyes to sunlight. She peered to her side to see Brier still asleep. She shook him. "Up you go. You still need to train." Brier mumbled but got up. After a breakfast of bread and apples, which she had packed, he practiced swings and thrusts.

"It's about time we sparred." Eliana pulled out two swords from her bag.

Brier froze. "Spar? Isn't that too dangerous?"

She pulled one of the swords from its sheath. "See? The end is blunted, and the blade is dulled." She sheathed it again. "The only injury would be from sheer force and it wouldn't be fatal. Besides, I packed chainmail for the fight against the Dragon."

"That still doesn't sound safe."

"Don't worry. The worst we can get is a few scratches."

"Right." Brier took a training sword.

"Then let's start." Eliana thrusted her sword.

Brier dodged and adjusted his stance to keep balance.

She exerted more and more force with every clash, and was soon pushing him back. Of course, it'd be easy to end the spar in a few seconds, but the goal was for Brier to learn and get stronger. That meant his endurance had to be good too.

Brier gasped between breaths as he dodged and stayed on the defensive.

"It's wise to defend but sooner or later, you need to strike back." Eliana swung her sword. Their swords clashed and his was flung away from the force.

He fell back on the ground, panting.

"Take a break, but we'll continue later." Eliana sat down next to him, handing out a water container.

Brier took it and gulped down half of it before giving it back.

"Come." She stood up. "We must continue on our journey."

They traveled further on horse. During breaks, she gave him more advice while they sparred. As they traveled, the land grew barren and there was no sight of any animals or people. The sun set below the horizon.

They camped and Eliana took out dried food. She peered at Brier, lost in thought. "What are you thinking about?"

He smiled, but it didn't reach its eyes. Eliana was familiar with that expression. She had always smiled like that, but his was filled with more sorrow. "This reminds me of the famine."

Eliana scooted closer. "You mentioned that before." She paused. "You said you were at an orphanage. What happened to your parents?"

Brier nodded. "I guess it's my turn for a long story."

He sighed. "During the famine, when I was younger, both of my parents worked to get food on the table. But even then, the taxes were too high. Since our village couldn't meet the tax deadline, the women were taken to serve the baron. The men in the village tried to fight back but the baron's knights slaughtered them. My dad died in the fight. And my mom was taken to the baron's estate."

"Who was this baron?" Eliana asked.

He smiled with more warmth in his eyes this time. "You probably don't remember but you ordered that baron to be executed, Baron Beckilt."

Eliana made a small hum. "Ah yes, that baron. He had the audacity to insult me and my mother at the annual ball, so I arrested him for treason and executed him." She placed a finger on her chin. "It was only after he was dead that the royal knights went through his estate and found slaves."

"My village was forever grateful for that and for the appointment of the far more considerate Baron Calia."

Eliana pursed her lips. She hadn't executed that fool for selfless reasons, but seeing Brier's smile made her a bit glad that she carried through with the order, even if it was met with the nobles' disapproval. She cleared her throat. "And ... what about your mother?"

"The knights returned her body to me." He looked down, his hair hiding his expression. "And I buried her under the oak tree next to the orphanage."

Her heart twinged. If only she had the power to protect her people...

Brier made a small smile. "It happened a long time ago. I can barely remember my parents' faces." He inhaled. "I remember how warm it was, though. When my mother hugged and sang me to sleep and how my father ruffled my hair and teased me."

149

Eliana's eyes became gentle. "That sounds rather nice." She laid down on a blanket, covered herself with another one, and looked back at him. "What did she sing?"

Brier brightened. "I remember her voice when she sang my favorite lullaby. It goes like this." He cleared his throat. "*My dear, the stars were waiting for you, for you to open your eyes. The moon was waiting for you, for you to smile. Don't cry, wipe your tears and look at the sky. The sun will wait for you, for you to be ready. So, stay here as long as you need to, my dear.*"

Eliana listened as he softly sang. She turned her head away but felt tears as she recalled her nanny singing the same song.

She fell asleep to his gentle voice without realizing it.

***

The next day passed uneventfully. She practiced with him along the way, still unsure how prepared he would be, or if he would be up to the task. She doubted it.

They would reach the Dragon's lair by nightfall. Eliana planned on camping nearby and attacking the dragon at dawn when there was enough light. She let Brier conserve his energy and walked beside him as he rode on Valiant.

As the sun set, they stopped to set up their final camp. Because they were so close, there would be no fire tonight. It would be too dangerous. She tied Valiant to a low bare tree and sat down next to Brier next to some withered shrubs nearby. In the distance, a mountain rose to the sky. The Dragon dwelled in a cave at the base. She felt the familiar stare from Brier, his eyes moving back and forth, hesitating on if he should speak. She figured they had gotten close enough that he wouldn't be so nervous, but it seemed not. "Go on," she said.

Brier stammered. "It's just that you looked tired and I uh—thought it'd be more comfortable if you took a nap leaning on my shoulder." He raised his voice during the last part, making it more of a question.

She paused. "Alright then." She didn't care too much about the gesture, but seeing Brier's surprised expression was amusing. She rested her head on his shoulder and closed her eyes. Eliana felt Brier tense up under her. "Relax. Didn't you want me to sleep?"

Brier relaxed his shoulders in response.

She started to hum the melody he sang last night and he joined in. After a few minutes, she fell asleep.

***

When she awoke, she saw Brier's panicked face. She jumped up and grabbed her bag. She sorted her thoughts out as Brier pulled her hand and they ran. They ran past the bushes and the trees and through an open clearing of dry grasses.
She had to pause to take a breath.

Then she smelled it. Smoke. Fire. She gritted her teeth and scanned the surroundings. The barren land. There was only dirt, a few bare trees, and dry bushes and shrubs, nothing to take shelter. Without planning on it, they were now right in front of the Dragon's lair, a ring of fire preventing their escape.

She tugged Brier's hand back. "We have to go into the cave."

"Where the dragon is?" he shouted incredulously.

She hurried ahead. "Do you see the fire behind us?"

Brier paused, and she stared at him. That was enough for him to follow her into the cave, where they soon found a large cavernous room. Eliana motioned to the Sword of Fate. Brier unsheathed it and held it out. The Sword's blade burst into flames and cast light on the walls and ground. He yelped and almost dropped the sword.

Eliana held onto his hand without a word. After he calmed down, she looked towards him. "You're the Hero. It's not going to burn you. Let's keep walking."

As they went further, it became warmer. Beads of sweat gathered on their faces reflecting the fire from the Sword.

Then they saw it. The Dragon had been waiting for them.

Red scales glimmered in the light of the Sword. It towered over them; their bodies each the size of one of its talons.

Its vertical pupils dilated as it gazed down on them. The Dragon's eyes narrowed at the Sword and roared. The ground shook under their feet.

The Dragon's head rose and it bellowed out fire.

Eliana pushed Brier out of the way. She ducked under the flame and rushed towards the Dragon, dodging talons and more flames. She hid

151

behind a rock, her clothes torn and singed. The heat in the cave surged and suffocated her. She breathed in; a rush of dizziness stilled her.

At that moment, the Dragon charged at Brier. He ducked and rolled to the side but dropped the Sword. The Dragon inhaled, about to release a torrent of fire.

Eliana ran towards Brier and grabbed the Sword on the way. It didn't matter that the hilt would burn her. She couldn't let him die.

The Sword deflected the Dragon's flame. It threw its talon up and roared.

She lunged forward at the Dragon. All she saw was red. It burned her eyes and throat. The Sword flashed a blinding light and the red became brighter, obscuring her vision.

When she opened her eyes, the Dragon had collapsed, dead, its body already disintegrating into magic that would nourish the barren land.

She looked around for Brier.

***

Arms around each other, Eliana and Brier limped out of the cavern, the smell of blood following them. They made their way back to their camp in a stunned silence. She stared at her hands.

"Good job back there," Brier said.

She looked up at him. "When I took the Sword, it didn't burn me."

"Maybe it's because you used it to save me?" He waved around with his hands. "You swung that sword at the Dragon out of the kindness of your heart."

"Kindness?" Eliana scoffed. "What a ludicrous reason." She glared at the Sword. "Even if all the chosen Heroes were kind, how could they continue to be, after committing murder?" She looked into the distance. "No one would describe my father as kind, yet everyone acknowledges that he was a strong Hero."

"You know, you've talked about your father, but what about your mother?"

"She died right after giving birth to me. But I've heard what she was like from others. A strong and determined person who'd do anything for her goals. After the Hero, my father, came back from slaying the Dragon, she got rid of all the other noble ladies vying to marry him."

"Really? But I thought the Hero always marries the Princess."

"Not all legends have to be followed. The Hero can choose who to marry, and my mother's ambition for power led her to him. Perhaps my defiance of the legends came from her."

Out of the corner of her eyes, she saw Brier fidgeting. "So, this means… I don't have to marry you?"

"Relax, I don't plan on marrying you. You wouldn't last a day against those cutthroat nobles and their politics."

Brier sighed in relief.

"What are you going to do when we get back?" Eliana asked.

Brier scratched the back of his head. "I guess I'll go back to my village."

She smiled. "If you're unsure, then why not consider working as the groundskeeper of the royal gardens?"

Brier's eyes lit up. "You mean that?"

Eliana chuckled. "It's only natural that I'd offer a good position for the Hero. When we return, let's celebrate with a banquet in your honor."

He shook his head. "I'm not the Hero, you are. You're the one who killed the Dragon."

"A shame that no one will believe that." She nudged him with an elbow. "Then, it's only natural that I'd offer a good position for Brier, my dear friend."

He grinned. "I wouldn't mind a banquet in honor of that."

ONLY AN IMITATION

by Kayla Nguyen

I took two photos,
same but different,
can you see?

With frost tipped branches,
white wisps of cold,
even brown tree stumps
seem white and old

Both are the same mountain top
but with contrasting tones that
manipulate what you see,
force you to doubt your beliefs

But here's a gift:
I'll free you from these framed,
laminated sheets.

Come to the mountains,
and decide for yourself.
What do you see?

A CONFESSION

by Brandon Nguyen

it is often that i think of myself,
in many ways, a tragic man,
for i hold no heroism.
only bad things happen to me
whether i deserve it or not,
and rarely, i do not.
'bad things happen for good reasons'
and all the other lies we tell ourselves.
living becomes a struggle in that world,
but we find that this is not where it ends

I'll stand up.
How tragic my fate is, I say
But I find it is not tragic at all.
I'll stand up from beneath
The rubble of my thoughts.
I'll stand above my fate.
I'll say, that's how it is,
And so be it.

My ultimate acceptance to find myself
For fate is only as tragic as the man it befalls
And all of us, we'll find our legs.
We'll find our wings, and if they don't exist,
Then we'll be happy that we struggled,
For that is enough to fill our hearts.

SUN THIEF

by Keanu Hua

"AND SO, LET THIS young one be sacrificed!"

Father's knife plunged into the lamb, its blood pooling onto the altar table in the town square. And in that moment, I felt, I knew, that something about this—our annual tradition—wasn't right.

Every year, all 200 or so members of my family would gather in the square to sacrifice a lamb to the Sun for a good harvest.

Never liked it. I'd always been the one in charge of caring for the lambs, so I grew to see killing a defenseless creature as cruel, especially one that had been raised by my hand. Course, I didn't want to offend Father with my heresy. After all, the man raised me. I was his son.

If not for the delivery men and the occasional visitor from outside, I wouldn't have known sacrificing lambs was not how the rest of the world worked. I thought our ways were wrong, but as the pastor's son, I knew better than to challenge him.

When I was thirteen, though, we inducted some 300 more to our flock. Then, Father called for me one evening, while I was out in the fields, beneath the shade of a tree, my head against my sleeping lamb.

"Tammuz."

At that, my lamb rose, and my head bumped against a low hanging branch. This lamb, Tzukim, had always been a strange one—nobody else knew where he came from, and he always wandered off at night. Except, when I came out to get him, I swore I'd see him stand for a moment, amber eyes staring at the Moon, and then he'd look at me and smile a human smile. Perfect human teeth. Then, he'd be back on his hind legs, and I'd wake up in bed. Surely, a dream.

Sometimes, I'd swear that I heard him say "freedom" between bleats.

"I understand that your lambs are precious to you," Father said, "but we need a sacrifice. The neighboring clan has already sacrificed their cows in order to ruin us. Have you seen any rain the past few months? Have you heard of what has happened to Malcolm's family?"

I stared at the rising Moon. Father was right, that I knew; the rains would have already come by this time of year, but there had been none so far, and the fields had grown brown and dry. Malcolm's daughter had also fallen sick with... something. No one knew what it was, not even the village physician.

My lamb kicked around in my arms. I stayed silent. Father's knife flashed underneath his robes. "I need as many lambs as possible for this. Tomorrow, we will lose a generation of lambs, but the Sun... She will avenge what we had lost. She will save our land and Malcolm's child."

I nodded. Inside, I knew that he had crossed a line. Sacrifice all our lambs, they'll sacrifice all their cows back in vengeance. Then what?

All of our crops? Ourselves?

I had to run.

I learned from old ruins that there had been people like us here before. I'd stumbled across their bones, personal effects, and journals, all showing that they sacrificed everything to destroy one another. Crops, livestock, even their own children. But it didn't matter in the end. They all died in vain.

This was the path that Father was walking.

"Very well, Father. If it will please you."

He turned to leave. I watched him disappear behind the door of the house, and I sat in the grass, lamb at my side. I stroked his cheek, and he bleated before I stood and motioned for him to follow. I sighed. I knew I couldn't stop him, so I would have nothing to do with it. All I could do was save myself and my lamb.

I would have to leave Father.

Tzukim started wandering off.

"Hey, come back here."

But he kept going. I stood up and followed him, past the fences.

The lamb broke into a sprint. "Tzukim!"

Past the brush, past trees, past old ruins, past that moonlit stream. Where was my little lamb taking me? As much as I feared what awaited us in the woodlands beyond almost everything that I had ever known, I knew that I'd have to go into it eventually, because it meant my freedom and my lamb's safety. I couldn't leave without him: the family would find him, kill him.

And I couldn't let that happen.

Soon enough, I found myself beneath the eroding doorway of a ruined building. It was once a temple dedicated to a now long-forgotten god, its worshippers, too, dead and gone. Upon the dais, my lamb stood upon two legs. He looked back at me and smiled.

"You came, Tammuz," my lamb said. From a crack in the crumbling ceiling poured in the light of the dazzling Moon, illuminating my lamb—painting him holy. "This is thanks. For caring for me after I left home." A portal appeared behind him. "This is my world."

"Tzukim ... what?" Suddenly, all of those strange dreams began to make sense.

"Freedom. I came to find someone. If one person cared for me, I would free them from Her—the Sun." The dais glowed, and the beams of moonlight reflected upon my lamb, who reared his front legs. "Join me. Become one with me."

As much as I wanted to run ... well, if I destroyed my family's belief in Her, wouldn't that make us free? Wouldn't that save Father from his desire for vengeance? Keep my lambs safe?

"As long as this doesn't hurt my family." My eyes hardened with determination. "Okay." I grasped my lamb's leg. "I will."

The arcs of moonlight grew brighter as brilliant beams of otherworldly light beamed upon us from behind the portal. A blinding pain scorched my entire body, and I shrieked as a pair of ram's horns grew from the temples of my head. My lamb stumbled, hunching over. He seemed to feel my pain.

Power flooded me. The moonlight grew brighter, until it became its own sun, and the stone walls and ruins disintegrated against its brilliance, until the entire structure was gone.

Then, we flew apart, and I slammed against the cobbles, feeling nothing except a slight daze. But Tzukim. I watched as he disintegrated to dust, where he sat crumbled against what remained of the dais. He was gone. All of that and for what? For my lamb to die?

But then, my hair ruffled, yet there was no wind. I felt a presence all around myself.

"Tammuz." It was Tzukim's voice, fainter than air, speaking as if across a veil. "I am here. From my body and in your hand, my power. Use it."

I ran back to town, the moonlight illuminating my path. Would my family fear me? Worship me? Whatever the case, I knew I had to take this chance to destroy the altar, which Father said stored our souls for the Sun's service. Destroy it, liberate everyone.

I blitzed past the houses, past the familiar faces of my family as they stared at me in horror. They pushed, pulled each other this way and that, trying to save themselves from my path, but I wasn't blinded by my goal. I had no interest in hurting them, at least, not physically. I knew that our "family" had lives before the Sun stole them.

By the time I got to the altar, news spread fast enough that Father was there, knife over a lamb from the marketplace, sunlight blasting over him. "Our Sun, defend us from this ungodly—"

I felt power radiate out from me, fly skyward in a brilliant beam of moonlight. It shone over him, and the sunlight dissipated. The lamb's bindings snapped, the altar crumbled into dust, and Father fell to the ground. So much for the strength of the Sun.

With that done, I clambered up the altar, and stood next to Father. He stared at me, eyes wide in disbelief and rising anger. "Who …" he sputtered.

I slammed my shoe on his chest. "You've lied to all of them, Father." He gasped. "Tammuz?"

I leaned down. "It's never worked on me. I knew better than you." Now, I turned to the crowd, and felt the nighttime chill wrap around me as the sun set. "Everyone! Your Sun is false. You have been slaughtering lambs for nothing, and now Father seeks vengeance through sacrifices that will do nothing—look at the ruins to see what I mean." My eyes passed over the crowd. Shock, fear, revelation.

I raised my hand, and a beam of moonlight cleared a path through the woods, away from the mountains; from the maps Father had, I knew it'd take them to other settlements and civilizations. "Now, free yourselves

159

from your false beliefs. Find your families, all of those you left behind for Father's lies."

The mystified crowd looked around. A few trickled towards the illuminated path. Then a crowd, everyone except Malcolm's family. So, I looked down at Father. He was afraid.

Powerless. I extended a hand to him, but he merely glanced at it before looking back up to me. He gave the empty square a final look, realization finally hitting him.

With nothing left for him, he scrambled to his feet and into the woods, but away from my moonlit pathway. Seems I had to go without him.

I touched a hand to one of my horns as Tzukim bleated in my head. The horns sank away, but still his presence remained within me. Hearts bound.

I stepped down from the rubble and paused as Malcolm straggled out, carrying his daughter. Her pallor was much milder, but somehow, I knew there were better doctors out there, somewhere outside our little cult home that could help them. Once those two were out of sight, I started down my path.

Here began my journey toward a new world. I'd find my way, find others beyond my village who would rather love than hurt.

THOUGHTS

by Makea Linh Adams

(Inspired by "Arrangement in Gray and Black," painting by James Whistler)

The poor woman sat in silence,
Waited years for a change,
Wondered if life was on her side

She wanted a new start
But they tied her down

Tired of her circumstances,
Sat in thought of what to do
Stared at the painting hoping she was there
A change of scenery

The world outside was daunting,
Her closed blinds kept her safe

She longed for a change, her home was sacred
The only place she could be true

Sitting for years at a time
Her world bored her

This is no way to live
Freedom wasn't a word she knew
What would happen if she fled?

Should she flee and start again?

PURPOSE GIVEN, PURPOSE LOST

by Jacqueline Truong

I was given life with one purpose.

> "Guardian angel—lead him to heaven,
> the land of forgiveness: his battle scars
> may close here, all to be forgotten."

> the single means of escape
> from the broken, lawless land below
> earth, once loved; never again.

> and yet the mortals would carry on
> breathing, exhaling, the fiery air.
> was I supposed to pity them?

I was given form with one purpose.

> I descended upon that shattered plain, of
> skeletons of trees, graveyards of grass
> that was all you had known for days of wandering.

> "come. come with me to heaven,
> the land of forgiveness: your battle scars
> may close there, all to be forgotten."

> only sometimes, I'd learn, the invitation
> works. other times it doesn't—but you have
> no choice; you must come along anyway.

I was given memory with one purpose.

> I remember the first time you died,
> at the hands of the demons
> and yet, I didn't even cry.

perhaps I'd saved those tears
for the next time we met:
another chance to do things right.

after all, you didn't remember the
way that the beasts devoured you.
your life, then, was in my hands.

I was given life with one purpose.

to welcome a weary soul into heaven, to
put a mortal to rest, lest he continue
waking up in this cycle of life and death.

but that second time, the elements took
you instead. was I supposed to learn?
what was there to remember but pain?

death always followed life. a sad revelation
realized. yet I found myself enjoying the warmth
of the sun as it beamed onto the land.

I was given form with one purpose.

to be able to walk on the earth, to lead him
on the right path. lest he continue to
wander endlessly, trapped on mortal plains.

but the third time, I found myself trying
to hold your hand. it was warm.
an unfamiliar sensation—yet still pleasant.

not even the sun had the warmth that
you had. not all angels would have the
privilege to feel another body.

I was given memory with one purpose.

I knew, now, we would meet again
and again. no matter how many times
you died and fell through my hands.

it would only all end if we ever reached
the paradise above. each perilous journey
a means of improving the next.

duty fulfilled, but my life and form lost.
my time with you lost, never to hold your
hand again. regardless of whether it was warm or cold.

what, then, would serving my purpose mean?

I let the demons take you that third time—
there would still be a fourth chance, after all.
not only for salvation, but for a chance at your love.

OH SOLDIER

by Ery Nguyen

Steps onto untouched lands
Marks on trees by unskilled hands
Along the path lay broken swords
Bodies upon bodies of fallen hordes

Over by the crystal lake
A single figure stands awake
In their hands a single saber
Bloody and rusted with untold labor

Rumor spreads about the wanderer
Some say, "A simple ponderer"
But in their eyes a weary glint
Their fighting skills as strong as flint

Up on a hill, an old grave lay
The stone stands strong both night and day
Flowers bloom across the field
Once a barren land to those who yield

Oh, soldier there, who stands and cries
Tears stain the grave, under bright blue skies
Battles fought long ago
Now without a place to go

They wipe their face and turn away
They must live another day

THE LIFE OF A DOLLMAKER
by Keanu Hua

MOST KIDS AT THIS middle school know me as "the guy with fifty dolls in his room." They're right, but that doesn't mean that it's got to be my one defining trait, even if Dad had been making them since I was born. "Family business," he called it.

Only that little suburban front yard, with the old hickory at the cul-de-sac center, that my friends and I used to play in, or that pool in the back? Same property that staged a whole … affair, which was how I got my nasty scars, why a whole house went boom, and why I live with Grandpa now.

I had always known Dad loved dolls, and Mom was dead, and that there was a ball-jointed doll in a wedding dress that looked just like her, sitting on my nightstand. He said it was to keep her spirit alive. Beside that doll, there was the Civil War soldier with the little toy-cap rifle, the farm boy, the cyborg, the assassin, the songstress, all ball-jointed, all made before I was born...

Even back then, I had a feeling they all meant more than just works of art. Same with every other doll in my room—whether they were made of bisque, plastic, or cloth, each of them felt alive in some way. Now, most people get weirdly scared by the idea of a living doll thanks to all those horror films out there about some ghost-doll coming alive to shank people—but for me, who had tons of nightmares, usually of Dad turning into a monster, I found that waking up to find a doll snuggled up in my arms or a doll's hand over my head... it was calming, somehow. They never felt like a threat.

When I was six, I asked Dad about it, but he just shrugged. "You probably just pull them off your shelf when you're asleep," he would always say.

I didn't believe him, but there wasn't much I could do instead, anyway. Although, if they were really alive, they could've at least done my homework, too.

Anyway, there were a lot more dolls scattered around the house, including some downstairs that always looked at Dad and I whenever we walked around down there, but they never did that with visitors. Figured Dad must've told them to be careful, or maybe they knew to be careful, or else we'd probably get our house scoured by some weirdo trying to exorcize our "evil dolls" or something like that.

Sometimes, we got guests like businessmen and government people; well-dressed and sharp, but they only ever came at night. I never spoke to them, but they always sounded tired when I heard them downstairs. I needed a glass of water one night, when I was around eleven. But I paused at the top of the stairs. Heard them.

"Your shipment will be ready in another night, sir," Dad said. "Thank you for your continued support."

Step-step-step.

Our petrified-wood front door slammed shut, and down I went, popped open the fridge, and turned right round to see Dad coming from below, silent.

"Oh, Daniel." He set his hand on the desk next to the door. "You probably shouldn't be down here right now. I'm at work."

"What kind of work that you can't—"

"Give it a year," he said. "Babies become kids become teens become adults, and we like it less every step of the way." He looked away. "Some of us don't even get to become adults."

"What?" He had that weird habit of saying random stuff like that.

He chuckled. "I mean I'd rather be a doll than an adult." His weight shifted, and he walked to the kitchen, opening and shutting cupboards. "Point being, don't hurry adulthood, Daniel. I enjoy my work, but sometimes …"

"Do you mean the dolls?" I asked. "I mean, why can't I help now? I can make them, too."

His hazel eyes stared at me. "Because it just isn't time yet."

I leaned forward, but something felt off as I looked back into him,

167

like all of his authority came out of his eyes, and that I shouldn't talk. But talk I did, because I was that kind of kid at the time. "But why?"

"As I said, don't hurry things. It's …" He waved his hand aimlessly. "Like driving. Or voting. We don't trust kids with either. Work, kind of the same way, mine especially. Besides …" He tilted his head. "As much as I'd like to tell you, I have an NDA on this one."

"NDA?"

"Non-disclosure agreement. Companies have big secrets, Daniel," Dad said. "Secrets they don't want their competitors to get a hold of. Why else do you think I get so much money from dollmaking? I've got my share of secrets for it, and if you know my secrets, and you talk to your friends about it, I can get into … a bit of trouble."

"Go poof?"

He laughed and opened the fridge, taking out a plastic bottle of kombucha. "Yep, just like that. Well, I think I'd just lose my job, but speaking of which, I've got to get back to it."

I stepped next to him and lightly pulled at the hem of his shirt. "But next year, right? You'll tell me then?"

He patted my head. "Of course."

The next year came, and I turned twelve. After that, Dad began working a lot more, and the usual group of visitors—homeless and business alike—came weekly, sometimes daily. It was much more often than their past monthly visits.

In September, just when school started and I went up to Elijah Intermediate, Dad said his clients were lodging more requests than usual. His hazel eyes trailed toward the letter, sitting on the coffee table.

"Does it have something to do with that letter?" I asked.

He smiled. "Remember what I said last year, that you would be able to join me in work?" I nodded. "Would you like to help me make an order?"

I gasped, grinned, and nodded.

"Good." He led me into the basement and set a sketch and doll armature on one of the two tarp-covered tables in the center of the room—a two-foot large doll, and I smiled. Thinking of the dolls he had shown me, I realized these must be the biggest dolls he had ever sold.

"Who're these for?" I pulled the bucket of clay towards me and opened it.

"Old friend of mine." He looked up. "Oh, don't use the standard clay. He wanted something …" Dad took out another container of clay, which looked white and shiny in the yellow light, and set it on my counter. "This stuff."

"Where's that from?"

He was walking back to his table. "His own country."

"Which is.?"

Dad glanced up as he set the first bits of clay around his armature. "He never told me, and the postal service won't, either."

Now that was strange. "Are you sure this friend isn't like…. I grabbed a piece of clay, but…why was it colder than usual? "Someone dangerous? Like, why would he—"

"He's just a private man," Dad said. "That's all—doesn't like being followed by anyone."

I nodded, and grabbed another chunk of clay, rolling it over the armature, then paused. Hadn't I forgotten something?

Another hit of clay on the armature, and then I straightened up. "I just remembered," I said, "I have a math test, and I really—"

"Do you want me to help you study?"

I hurried over to the sink and washed my hands. "You look busy, Dad. Shouldn't you—"

"That's not a problem, Daniel, I'm freelance for a reason, and I can spend a day with you just fine." He came to my side and washed his hands. "Come on, let's go."

The months flew by, the two of us shaping the odd clay and firing and glazing our dolls, all the while I saw fewer and fewer people who were homeless–must've been either the weather or some luck with the lottery.

Course, by November, when the police started reporting a kidnapper menacing them, I figured there was something up, but whatever the case, it was enough for Dad to tell me to be at least a little more careful, especially since he said that he'd seen someone suspicious snooping around.

Soon, my thirteenth birthday came by, and right after school, Dad picked me up with two vanilla cakes in the trunk of the car that elicited a pat on the back from Rolf, my ginger-haired best-friend.

"Nice cake, bro."

I whirled around and caught his hand mid-pat, smirking. "I'm not your 'kiddo' anymore." Rolf had always seen me as so much younger, considering I was born December 31st and he was born January 13th, and he was a head taller. Both of which he loved to remind me of.

"Rolf." Our other friend, Camille, stepped between us and chopped our hands apart, her flowing platinum-blonde hair brushing against our arms. "It's too nice of a day to pick on him."

Rolf rolled his eyes. "Please, if he's not 'my kiddo anymore,' he can take a few pats."

"But on his birthday?" Camille said. "Are you ser—"

"Kids," Dad called, "we're holding up the other cars."

We piled in and drove to my place, and the moment we arrived, Rolf took off his shirt, ducked into the bathroom, and seconds later he was sprinting toward the pool in swimming trunks.

"Rolf!" Camille said. "Don't run in other people's hou—"

He spun around. "Hey, don't—ow." His face smacked against the glass door, still unopened, and Camille laughed. After a few steps, I saw two of the dolls on one of our cabinets looking at them from behind, eyebrows knitted in what looked like worry.

They'd never done that before. I stared at them, and they turned their heads towards the stairs, towards my room, but I didn't feel hostility from them. If anything, all I felt from them was that something was about to happen, I guess, like something would happen that day that I wouldn't be able to go back on.

But still, I went upstairs, and got into my room. On my nightstand was the cyborg doll, but I was pretty sure I had left him up on the shelf, so I set him back there, turned all my dolls to face the wall, got changed, grabbed my whistle-necklace and goggles, and hurried downstairs. Camille had just gotten changed, and was walking out to the pool where Rolf was already splashing around.

"Jump on in you two," he yelled. "I can't entertain myself!"

Camille grabbed a beach ball at her side, one that I had left out in the backyard. "How's this for entertainment?" She hurled the ball, and it struck Rolf, and I watched as his head knocked backwards. "Daniel, you got another?"

I passed her a second one, and she smirked as she dribbled it on the tiles. "Hey, catch!" She threw it again. Hit again. This time, he was shoved enough that his legs flew up into the air.

What a tool.

While those two fought, I headed over to the shed and pulled open the doors, then grabbed a set of water guns. There were a few good lawn chairs in there. I threw the water guns on the floor, and then took the top of a chair's metal seat, dragging it out of the shed.

I yelped when I felt a wet hand reach from my right side and grab my own hand. "Rolf!"

"So about you still being small and all …"

"Huh." I let go of my chair and playfully shoved him, laughing as he stumbled in the grass.

He rubbed his side and grimaced. "Eh … maybe I shouldn't have done that."

My phone, still in my pocket, buzzed with a text message.

More friends at the door.

"Right, can you guys set up the chairs? I'll get the door." I headed in and glanced at the cabinet. The dolls were gone, but I figured Dad must have moved them. Too scary, something like that, even when most of my friends at my party were the sorts that could or would sooner punt or throw them than be scared of them.

Not that I'd let them.

Eventually, there were a good eight of us at the pool. There were the badminton king and queen, as we called them, the footballer who had a purple-streaked side bang that he called "an identifying feature," the acrobat girl … somehow, I had gotten mixed up with most of the top sports kids at Elijah Intermediate despite being a middling swimmer, at best, not that I had issue with it.

But we had about thirty water guns, and if there was one thing that I was definitely good at, it was water gun fights—I wasn't the kind of big, bulky guy who would get hit easily, unlike Rolf. Usually, it was me prancing around for a couple minutes in a four versus one.

"Rolf, Camille." I grabbed the first water gun and gestured to the hoses. "Let's get this started." A few minutes later they were all filled with my house's usual cold water, and Rolf rushed to the shed. This time, he grabbed a floatie and threw it into the pool. Then, the three of us grouped all of the water guns and set them on the floatie, pushing it into the center of the pool.

Everyone arrayed themselves on the edges of the pool. Some stood farther back than others for a running start, and some were at the very edge, knees bent, ready to jump.

I slapped my goggles on. "Ready! Set!" I breathed in.

Fwwtt!

The pool resounded with kids jumping in. Rolf was first and fastest, and I watched as he surged forward for his water bazooka, then dove underneath. I, meanwhile, grabbed a couple of water pistols, something quick and easy that I could maneuver with, then plunged into the waters as well.

At my side, Rolf was swimming perpendicular from me, and I continued my path, glancing forward then back at Rolf. His bazooka wasn't something I wanted to get a hit from.

Once at the deck, I thrust myself out of the water, and turned to my side to check on Rolf. His bazooka was inches from my face, threatening a chilly demise.

"Rolf, please, I have a family of dolls I need to get back to."

He set down the bazooka.

"Thank God."

"I'll blast you at the next pool party, but today—"

"Wait, stop, stop!"

I turned left; one pistol raised. It was the football player and badminton duo, and the footballer was speaking with his own bazooka at his side. "Rolf, you can't do this again."

"Do what?"

"Are you seriously playing dumb?" Footballer aimed. "You do this every time. Find Daniel, say you're his knight—just because you're his friend doesn't mean you can just give him a vic—"

Behind him, I could see badminton duo raising their weapons, and footballer's hand was on the trigger. Before I could see anything, Rolf

172

shouted.

"Get down, Mr. Birthday Boy!" He tackled me into the pool, and I watched as he endured the volley of shots. Meant for me.

Just before I fell all the way in, I saw Camille running towards them, rifle pointed. Sure, it was against the rules for any of us to team up in a free-for-all like this, and I felt at least a little bit bad for the others; I was good, not a cheater.

Flailing around in the pool, I saw Dad watching from the window and I couldn't help but wonder: did he have his own friends? He had never talked about them, and with other parents, I never felt like he was all there, like he couldn't quite bring himself to open up. I looked up again and Dad was gone.

I couldn't think about it for long, not when Rolf dove in and picked me back up to play round after round, and soon enough, it was six, the sun was set down low, winds were getting a bit too chilly for our soaked bodies, and everyone was about ready to rest. One-minute timers for each person in the bathroom to wash off the chlorine.

When we were all done, Dad came upstairs from the basement, and I saw a giant tray of spaghetti, along with another one of salad. One of them had the farm boy doll next to it, plus a handwritten note wishing me happy birthday. He set the trays down and left the room.

I glanced down at the note. It wasn't Dad's handwriting.

"What's he here for?" Camille said pointing to the doll.

I shrugged, headed upstairs, and set the doll on my bed, then shut the door. Dad was there, setting my wedding-dress doll on the counter, folded letter in hand. "Oh, Daniel," he said, turning around, "I was looking for you."

"For what?"

Dad smiled. "Remember the two dolls we've been making?"

All of my dolls were staring at him.

"Yeah."

"Would you like to show your friends to them later tonight? I'm almost done finishing up both, and I think it'd be nice if your friends got to see." He strode to the door and opened it. "Your debut."

"Does that matter a lot to you, Dad?" I asked. "Oh, and can I see that

173

le—"

"It matters to us." He closed the door.

Then something fell on the floor. I looked over, and all of my dolls had fallen off their shelves, their faces all turned in my direction. When did they move?

The farm boy was right next to an aged, dusty photograph of my father and six others in front of a boat, and the cyborg and the assassin formed a U and an S in front of it.

Us.

I stared down at them. Were they trying to tell me something?

The door budged behind me. "Oh, Daniel—"

Dad's eyes drifted down to the dolls, and I glanced back at him. Something about the way his eyes bore into me … moved me, so I picked up the songstress and set her back on the shelf. Before I knew it, all of my dolls were back on their shelves as if nothing had ever happened.

It was only when he left again, and I was outside my door, that I realized that I had no idea what I just did. Or what the dolls did. What did they mean by "us"?

I bumped into Dad in the hallway. "Dad?"

He turned around.

"Why did those dolls—"

"I made them … I made them in honor of my friends." He sighed. "To remember them, but … let's not talk about that, okay? Not on a day like this." He gave a sad smile, and his eyes drifted to the living room portrait of his wedding day. "Just make sure you treasure yours, okay? Memorialize them—who they were, how they sounded, alive, things like that."

I nodded, knowing he was having one of those moments where he tries to sound profound or something, then headed downstairs, where Rolf waved at me from the dining table. "Yo, birthday boy?" he said. "Where were you?"

"Oh, just cleaning my room a bit, that was all."

"On your birthday?" Camille leaned on the table, fork twirling a spiral of spaghetti. "You're kidding. Next time your dad asks you—"

"Let one of us take care of it," Rolf said.

"Yeah." She pushed him to the side with her hand on his face. "Sure. Him."

Footballer facepalmed, and the badminton duo next to him snickered. "Hey, lovebirds, let's get started on this party."

"Lovebirds?" Both Camille and Rolf rose. "Why don't you pick on the pair next to—"

I dashed forward. "Guys, guys, let's get to eating, all right?" I took my seat at the table. "So come on." Once that was done, everyone split off into their own little groups, and I, of course, stayed with Rolf and Camille.

"Oh, right, Rolf." I took a bite of my food. "About that argument with footballer earlier, uh … don't push the bazooka towards me next time, okay? Keep it nice and fair."

"Really?" He wiped his stained lips down with his fork. "I mean, I did, but it was just because you're my friend."

"That wasn't my point. I want a fair and equal fight, and if you're helping me, that's not that fair anymore, is it?"

He had an odd expression on his face.

Camille sighed. "I know that you're attached and all, but you should know by now how jealous everyone else can get when Daniel wins because of you."

"Hey, it was only once, and it was only a little bit."

She shook her head. "Once every pool party."

Rolf bit his lip, and I patted his shoulder. He sighed and turned away.

Once we finished eating, I got two cakes out with Camille's help. A quick birthday song later, half-hearted from some, half as a joke from the others, and then I cut one cake, while she did the other. Rolf sat at the dining table. Thinking.

Some left—acrobat-girl and footballer—but most of us stuck around in our own little groups, except Rolf was more distant than usual.

"Rolf," Camille said, "are you really that mad?"

"I'm not mad." He crossed his arms. "Absolutely not, I'm just …"

She sighed and swept her hair aside. She had a faraway look in her eyes, as if she were trying to look for the right words to say. "Upset?" She finally said. "Is it your family?"

"Rolf," I said, "you can trust—"

"It's not trust, it's just … I don't feel like talking about it. Not today."

I nodded. "But we'll still be here when you do."

He smiled.

Eventually, the partygoers started filing out. The badminton duo was out, scuffling as they left. Soon, it was just Rolf, Camille, and me, for our sleepover, the two of them on my floor with some blankets. Right after a few rounds of *Bash Bros*, where Camille gave a serious beat down to Rolf.

Once I had showered and headed towards my room, Dad came up from downstairs. Red glaze was all over his apron, and his fingers brushed against my shoulder.

"Hey, Dad."

"I'm almost done, Daniel, but it'll be a bit more before I get the finishing touches in."

"How long?"

"A few hours." He stepped past me. "But … I can't wait, Daniel." He smiled and stalked off to his room. It seemed he was busy, so I headed into mine.

Somehow, both of my friends were already asleep, so silent, I could barely hear them breathing. On my bed was the Civil War soldier holding a letter. I knew that he wasn't supposed to be there, so I picked it up.

The first page had an ethereal, wispy seal across all of it, but the rest of it was in English.

Dearest friend,

The condition of my twins is near critical. The doctors cannot do much else. I need you and your dolls. Prof. Valley has finished designing a way to mimic near-human locomotion, speech, growth, and thought that can be placed within a ball-joint. Enclosed are the plans, and passports for you and your son if you must need them. Rest assured all airline and police services have been accounted for, so he and you will be protected in case of emergency. I do not know nor care how you acquire the final components, but you will do this.

Understand what is at risk.

Adieu.

What … what did Dad need to do that needed 'all airline and police services' to be accounted for? And the twins—was I making them? But if I was, why did my ball-jointed dolls look the exact same as any other? They didn't have the level of joints that a person had, and yet—

Human speech, growth, and thought.

I looked down at Camille and Rolf, then at my dolls. In my concentration, they had all wandered onto the bed, and the bride was holding the same photograph as earlier.

Her clumsy fingers cracked, pointed. The cyborg and the assassin stood up and displayed their U and S once more. Then I realized.

But Dad couldn't—he wouldn't do that to someone, would he? I turned on the lights. Behind me, my bedroom door opened, and I turned back around, locking eyes with Dad's hazel ones. For a few moments, my vision blurred. I blinked.

When I opened my eyes again, I was back on my bed. All of my dolls were gone.

So were Rolf and Camille. I sprang out and ran downstairs. I looked up at the living room clock.

Midnight. I had showered at eight.

I looked at the basement, then heard a squadron of steps behind me. There were my six dolls—cyborg, songstress, soldier, bride, assassin, farm boy—all marching together in sync, four holding the laptop, two holding the mouse. On the screen was an article from some twelve years ago, around March.

"Sole survivor of boating accident," I muttered beneath my breath. The dolls holding the mouse scrolled down.

The photograph was the same one that they had shown me earlier. The same one that had read, "us."

Now it seemed to be the identifier for Dad's friends. I didn't know them, but I could feel them in front of me. They really were alive.

No wonder the bride reminded me of my mom.

I clenched my fist and whirled around, slamming open the basement door. Maybe Dad thought it was a gift to live again, but like this? As something nobody could talk to and most would be terrified of?

I hurried down the stairs. "Dad!"

"Oh, Danie—" He paused, and I heard the steps of my doll troop.

177

His apron was stained with the same red glaze as before, and I could see the twin dolls that he and I had made.

On the tables, tarps gone, were Rolf and Camille, eyes shut, ankles, wrists and chests tied down with flimsy padlocks

"Dad, what are you doing? Is this the or—"

"Sorry, Daniel." His hazel eyes and deep frown bore into me, and I felt the same disorientation as earlier. Something about his eyes—they were lulling me to sleep. Telling me to listen to him. That whatever he was doing, he was still my dad. "But this is for the best. Just do as I say, okay?"

I stepped forward, mouth dry and legs stiff. I didn't know what Dad wanted to do, but I felt like it wouldn't be right, that even if it were physically painless, I still couldn't do it. And yet I couldn't stop myself, not with Dad staring at me, as if his eyes were ordering me forward.

"There's just one step left, Daniel. Just one step before ..." Dad's words fell upon deaf ears.

"You're so lucky, Daniel. So lucky to have friends of your own. I only want to make sure you don't have to go through what I went through." His voice came low and echoing upon my ears, barely audible—distorted. "That's all."

Had I ever been afraid to lose them? The thought never occurred to me.

My head whipped in the direction of a multitude of footsteps against the stairs. There, at the steps, was my squadron of dolls, their ceramic eyes ablaze with a new vitality.

I jumped back from the lever, and looked back at my dad, who responded with an unreadable expression.

"Dad," I said, "what were you planning to do?"

He didn't answer.

"Was this ... your order?" This time, a nod.

"Don't worry, I don't need to remove all your friends' parts. I'll be able to put what's left into dolls of our own, and we can—"

I began a slow shuffle toward Rolf, careful not to let Dad notice. "And what about when I die? What about their parents? You can't just take the—"

"I can remove their memories, and after we ... 'disappear' from here, from that kidnapper, well, they'll just get new memories. That way, they'll think that we've always lived there. I'll just ... give a small piece of them to the order. That's all. He wants a happy family, so I'll—"

No more thinking. All action. My hand was on the first lock.

Dad rushed forward and grabbed my arm, pulling me away. His eyes glowed in the lamplight, locked in with mine, bore into me, but I continued to struggle against him as my other hand fumbled with one of the locks over Camille.

I wouldn't let him take my friends.

Then came the clatter of clay, and the dolls attacked. First came a cap, aimed at his throat, then the five others piled onto and leapt atop him, soaring in from behind me. Was this their revenge for being kept alive—trapped—like this?

I felt something metal hit my head, and I spun around. A key dropped into my hand, and I thrusted it into the first of the locks.

"Daniel!" Dad said.

One doll shattered, and I heard a faint cry. Not of hurt—but of relief.

"Help me!" Dad said.

I refocused and began unlocking the rest of Camille's restraints. When that was done, she sat up. Dad threw a second doll at my leg, and I heard another sigh of release. I fumbled against the table, and from below me, a glowing, wispy mass arose and dissipated into the walls. A spirit.

"No time to explain," I said, "get out of the house!" She rolled off of the table, I spun around, ran toward Rolf, and began unlocking him.

I flinched as a doll flew past my head, smashing into the wall in front of me. I whipped around to see where it came from. Dad stood there, heaving and hunched.

To my left, I heard a deep groan of something within the wall, then the sound of hissing gas and a terrible odor. Dad grabbed my leg, and I paused. He was still ... no, no. How could he think any of this was okay?

I kicked my other leg back, trampled over his wrist, and continued opening the locks.

"Daniel!" Dad yelled.

Another doll shattered.

"Daniel, stop this!"

I sprinted to the other side. A fifth doll broke, and soon enough, Rolf was out of there, and now it was my turn.

"Daniel …"

I couldn't help but turn around. Dad was battered all over and holding the bridal doll in the air. He hardly looked like the man who raised me anymore, not with the blood dripping into his eyes and tears down his cheeks, so much so that I couldn't even see them anymore. Were they glaring at me or her?

I ran. I remembered seeing a spirit hovering over the electric kiln in the corner.

I wiped a tear from my eyes. I wouldn't be able to stop them. Even if he was a monster, he was still my dad. He still taught me everything, and now …

I swallowed that thought and bolted through the door. Camille and Rolf were standing on the other side of the street, shivering.

And then, as I stepped onto the concrete of the sidewalk, my house exploded. I turned to see the fiery oranges and reds burning in the night sky, and felt the searing heat as I crumpled to my knees and passed out.

When I awoke a few minutes later, Camille and Rolf were holding me in embrace. I could hear sirens in the distance. For a few moments, I sat there, dazed, knowing nobody would believe me. Even then, not even I could, not at that moment. I only knew my childhood was lost to an inferno, and that all my dolls were gone.

The hardest part of it all was knowing that I would never see Dad again. And that it was all because of those dolls. Dolls of the people he lost, dolls that he made because he couldn't cope with losing everyone he loved. Dolls that my friends almost became.

What was it like to live like that? To only say "I love you" as a recording? To never be able to really make a memory as anything but a witness?

I couldn't imagine how painful that would be.

And I would never allow Rolf and Camille to live like that. Because that wasn't living.

WHAT DOES IT MEAN TO LIVE AS A HUMAN?

by Hillary Nguyen

Everywhere I see,
society thinks that I'm less than human,
That I might as well be
Some alien species
Or an unfeeling robot.

What do I feel?
Towards girls?
Guys?
People?
Nothing. I feel nothing.

Not the butterflies,
Not the rising heat,
Not a want or a need
That others describe.
Am I supposed to feel something?

And though I don't understand
And I'm not sure I ever will
I know that I'm
Just as human
As everyone else.

Labels:
To figure out who you are
And to find others, a community.

Sharing experiences.
That's a part of living, right?
The label I have now,
I didn't think it fit at first.

I never thought of it
as a possibility,
And assumed that it was normal
To not really care about
That kind of stuff
Until I was surrounded by questions.

"Who do you like?
What's your type?
How would you like to do it?"

I don't know.
I can't imagine it.
Who do I like?
What's my type?
How would I like to do it?

And I try to imagine
The situation where I'd be comfortable,
Vulnerable and yet reassured,
But I see that
The person in front of me
Is composed of abstract squiggles.
And I don't think
I'll ever really want to do it? With anyone?

Before I had thought
Well, I guess I just have to put up with it,
Put up with it and make whoever it is happy…
Right?

But there are options
And it would've been nice to know sooner
That there is more than just
Only one partner
Of the opposite sex
And making a family together.

That there are different kinds of love,
Not just romantic,
But platonic,
And different kinds of attraction,
Not just the one everyone
Instantly thinks of.

Labels:
Pick and choose
And see what fits
And I was afraid.
Was this too fast?
Am I too young to decide?
But no, that's not the case.
It's never too young or too old
To decide who I am.

When I first came out as who I thought I was,
It was fine. People understood,
Not just the opposite sex or the same sex,
Both and maybe more, that's okay.
But then the label changed.
That's not me, but I thought it was me.

This is me:
Not one or both or all, but nothing,
And then it was different,
Not like the first time,

Filled with understanding.

I realized that who I was
Was not a universal thing
And there was mostly support
But then there were
Preconceived notions of who I was
Because of the identity, the label I chose.

"Congrats on being alone forever."

Why did they say that?
Why did they assume my future?
Why did they assume that because
I felt nothing, I would be alone?

There are options.
Basking in solitude is fine,
But I think I would like company.
A partner? Maybe.

Maybe someone with a gentle smile
And warmth from hugs and cuddles.
Kisses, I don't know,
But I'd be happy with
one on the cheek or the forehead.

But those words, said by some,
That I will be alone, bite into me.
Little words, nonchalant, they mean no harm,
But I still don't like the feeling caused by such words.

I try to explain but I don't think the words carry through,
Through the air and to them.
Partly because I'm bad with words,

Partly because they really do think it's not a big deal.
Although I still remember those words
Lurking in the back of my head,
Making me feel not right,
Like there is something wrong with me,
While they've forgotten the exchange even happened.

The meaning of life
Has always been discussed and pondered.
To me, I think it means
To want to live
And prove others wrong.
Prove them wrong that
I am not a mistake,
I am not unnatural.

I should not feel guilty
For being me
Because of someone else's
Cutting beliefs.

I deserve to exist, to live,
As much as everyone else

Because I'm human too.

Even if I don't fit the norm,
Even if I can't understand the standard,
That doesn't make me less human
Than anyone else.

Then again,
Does there need to be
A reason to live?
Isn't just wanting to live enough?

AUTHOR BIOS

Makea Linh Adams
Makea Adams, resident of Westminster, loves to dance with her older sister, work on cars with her dad, explore culinary arts, and read stories about mystery and murder. One day she hopes to own a cafe.

Alham Attaee
A freshman at La Quinta High school, Alham Attaee finds that writing helps him stay focused. Inspired by his creative writing classmates, he strives to improve his craft. When he's not writing, he's playing soccer or hanging out with friends.

Sydney Dao
Born in Fountain Valley, California, Sydney Dao quickly developed a love for art in all forms at a young age. She continues to illustrate and write stories ranging from romance to horror to fantasy, and is steadily working to improve.

Isabella Guedes
Originally from California, Isabella Guedes grew up in Brazil where she discovered her passion for drawing, traveling, and writing. Moving to Westminster helped develop her writing skills from the last pages of her math notebook to the anthology. Isabella hopes to one day become a US diplomat.

Keanu Hua
Rooted in obscure references and dreams, Keanu Hua's brain is responsible for Rosetta-stoning his nonsense into intelligible English in his writing to fulfill the contract with his characters. When he's not relentlessly working as a journalist for La Quinta's yearbook, Keanu also publishes stories online.

Michelle Lam
Michelle Lam is a high school senior from Westminster, California who, although is uncertain about her path to adulthood, dreams of authoring a novel one day. When she's not writing or drawing, she hangs out with her sister, constantly waiting for summer.

Sonny Le

Sonny Le grew up near Beaumont, Texas with his brother and grandma but moved to California in search of a new start. He is unfairly biased to the color purple. Writing helps his brain stay active and he enjoys writing poems about his thoughts and interests.

Teresa Le

Teresa Le has a PhD in procrastination, sarcasm and wit. She tends to write sad, romantic poems and stories to represent the trials and tribulations of a breakup. Teresa loves the color blue and inserting sarcastic comments in conversation to create laughter.

Yathy Le

Sixteen years ago, Yathy Le spawned in California and has resided there ever since. She loves how art brings her ideas to life and now navigates the unfamiliar waters of writing with the hope that one day, she can use both skills hand-in-hand to create powerful stories.

Bethanie Luu

Born in Southern California, Bethanie Luu was heavily influenced by the literary arts and classics, something that inspired her to write stories of her own at a young age. Her growth can be seen in all the works she has published throughout her high school career.

Laura Miranda

Laura Miranda, born in California loves to draw, work with her brothers to fix their cars, read stories of romance, mysterious and history. She hopes to improve in track.

An Nguyen

An Nguyen was born in Vietnam and immigrated to America at the age of three. She grew up in Orange County and developed a love for writing and reading. Although oftentimes indecisive about the future, she has decided to study bioengineering.

Andy Nguyen

Since leaving his mother's womb, Andy Nguyen has not procrastinated on his homework his entire life. Despite his struggles in the past year, he aspires to be a Precalculus teacher. Although he is still studying the art of writing, he is confident in his creation of ideas and poetry.

Brandon Nguyen

Born and raised in California, Brandon Nguyen likes to read in his free time when he isn't working or playing games. In the future, he hopes to obtain a degree in creative writing.

Brian Nguyen

Born in North Carolina, Brian Nguyen moved to California where he developed a passion for gaming. He decided to take a creative writing course in his senior year of high school for fun. He hopes to establish a career in the military after college.

Caterina Nguyen

Born in Honolulu, Hawaii, and growing up in Westminster, California, Caterina Nguyen found a love for writing romance and drinking boba. She has a deep and passionate love for Root Beer. Caterina hopes to figure out what she wants to do or be before the start of her senior year.

Christine Nguyen

Since Christine Nguyen was young, she has had always had a creative side to her. With a strong belief in learning and improving, she joined this class to prove it. Now has a new passion for writing and would like to teach it one day.

Ery Nguyen

Born in Fountain Valley, California, Ery Nguyen has always had an imaginative mind that manifested in the form of stories and artwork. "Oh Soldier" is her first published poem. Ery hopes to have such luck with more fleshed out, longer stories.

Hillary Nguyen

Hillary Nguyen grew up in Fountain Valley, California where she developed an interest in writing and drawing. She expresses her fantasy-centered imagination, random thoughts, and emotions through her short stories and digital art. She hopes to further develop her art and writing skills and to also create comics.

Kayla Nguyen

Kayla Nguyen grew up in California where she developed her passion for writing stories ranging from paranormal fiction to fantasy. In her free time, she prefers to practice art, read, or play video games. This is her third time being featured in an anthology.

Kellan Nguyen

Kellan Nguyen has always been a creative person, spending their free time drawing illustrations and writing stories and poems about their original characters. They have an interest in fields of science, especially astronomy/astrophysics, which they hope to study in the future.

Mike Nguyen

Originally from Vietnam, Mike Nguyen moved to America when he was seven and developed a love for video games and music. Now, in his first year of high school, he's chosen to explore creative writing and looks forward to his first publication.

Stella Nguyen

Born and raised in California, Stella Nguyen, while living in Santa Ana, developed a knack for drawing, dancing, and gardening. She remembers writing stories in first grade class and wonders where they are now. In the future, Stella aspires to work with children.

Thien Nguyen

Thien Nguyen was born in Vietnam and came to America when she was 4. She wasn't fluent in English at first but eventually learned and fell in love with linguistics. This will be her first published poem. One of the things on her bucket list is writing a full-length book.

Vincent Quach

Author of two poems in *Abandoned Archives*, Vincent Quach is on a journey to find his place in this world. He's involved in many activities, from creative writing to long distance cross country to leadership in a unified PE class. He's a step closer to finding his purpose.

Khanh Tran

Khanh Tran grew up in Westminster where he developed a passion for writing. After having his poetry published in "Abandoned Archives," Khanh's skills in poetry return in "Inflorescence." Khanh hopes to continue writing after graduating high school.

Thomas Tran

Born in Westminster, California, Thomas Tran grew up in Santa Ana surrounded by a variety of artists and writers, and developed an interest in critiquing and editing the works of his friends. While he may not feel like a skilled writer yet, he prides himself on his capability as an editor.

Jacqueline Truong

Jacqueline Truong is an aspiring author with a passion for high fantasy settings and stories. She enjoys being able to express herself creatively, whether through writing, drawing or playing the piano. Having been previously published in two other LQHS Creative Writing anthologies, she strives to continue to share her works.

Madison Zinnekah

Born in Palm Springs, California, Madison Zinnekah spent most of her childhood in Westminster where she discovered her passion for writing alongside art. Although her writing was mainly left on the sides of her papers, she has a new drive to become a comic book artist.

Made in the USA
Coppell, TX
03 May 2022

77355182R00113